Florida Benchmarks Assessment Workbook

Grade 5

Scott Foresman·Addison Wesley

enVisionMATH™ Florida

Glenview, Illinois • Boston, Massachusetts • Chandler, Arizona • Upper Saddle River, New Jersey

Contents

ISBN-13: 978-0-328-46173-8

ISBN-10: 0-328-46173-3

6 7 8 9 10 V084 13 12

Name ____________________

Mark the best answer.

1 Which related multiplication equation makes it easy to find 480 ÷ 8? (1-1)

Ⓐ 8 × 6 = 48

Ⓑ 6 × 8 = 48

Ⓒ 8 × 60 = 480

Ⓓ 10 × 48 = 480

2 If $900 in gift certificates is shared equally by 9 people, how much does each person get? (1-2)

Ⓕ $10,000

Ⓖ $1,000

Ⓗ $100

Ⓘ $10

3 Tom wants to find 448 ÷ 4. How could he break apart 448 and find 448 ÷ 4 by using place value? (1-3)

Ⓐ (400 + 4 + 8) ÷ 4

Ⓑ (400 + 40 + 8) ÷ 4

Ⓒ (300 + 148) ÷ 4

Ⓓ (430 + 18) + 4

4 About 145 students are enrolled in 5 foreign language classes. About how many students are enrolled in each class? (1-4)

Ⓕ About 30

Ⓖ About 40

Ⓗ About 300

Ⓘ About 400

5 Linda is packing 358 toy cars in 9 boxes. She uses compatible numbers to estimate the number of toy cars she puts in each box. Which of the following expressions could she use to estimate 358 ÷ 9? (1-4)

Ⓐ 300 ÷ 9

Ⓑ 350 ÷ 9

Ⓒ 360 ÷ 9

Ⓓ 400 ÷ 9

6 The Johnson family drove their car 2,400 miles in 4 months. If they drove the same number of miles each month, how many miles did they drive each month? (1-2)

Ⓕ 6

Ⓖ 60

Ⓗ 600

Ⓘ 6,000

7 There are 88 students at a football game. The number of students who can sit in each row of bleachers is 9. Which answer is reasonable if you need to find how many rows of bleachers are needed so all the students have a seat? (1-7)

Ⓐ 10 rows since $88 \div 9 = 9$ with 7 left, and 1 more row is needed for the 7 left

Ⓑ 9 rows since $88 \div 9 = 9$ with 7 left, and the remainder can be ignored

Ⓒ 8 rows since you must subtract 1 from the quotient when you divide 88 by 9

Ⓓ 7 rows since the remainder is 7 when you divide 88 by 9

8 Mrs. Yager worked at a store for 150 hours in 5 weeks. She worked the same number of hours each week. Which related multiplication equation could you use to find $150 \div 5$? (1-1)

Ⓕ $5 \times 3 = 15$

Ⓖ $1 \times 150 = 150$

Ⓗ $5 \times 30 = 150$

Ⓘ $2 \times 75 = 150$

9 Sue wants to find $416 \div 4$. How could she break apart 416 and find $416 \div 4$ by using compatible numbers? (1-3)

Ⓐ $(415 + 1) \div 4$

Ⓑ $(410 + 6) \div 4$

Ⓒ $(400 + 16) \div 4$

Ⓓ $(400 + 1 + 6) \div 4$

10 Karen did sit-ups for 5 minutes a day, 4 days a week for 3 weeks. She did jumping jacks for 2 minutes a day, 3 days a week for the same number of weeks. How many minutes of sit-ups did Karen do in all? (1-5)

Ⓕ 60 minutes

Ⓖ 20 minutes

Ⓗ 18 minutes

Ⓘ 12 minutes

11 Julio is making balloon bouquets. He has 23 balloons. If he uses 5 balloons to make each balloon bouquet, how many balloon bouquets will Julio make? (1-6)

Ⓐ 2

Ⓑ 3

Ⓒ 4

Ⓓ 5

Go On

Name ______________________________

12 Pam is putting the 45 oranges she picked in baskets. She can fit 8 oranges in each basket. How many oranges will be in the last basket? (1-6)

0	0	0	0
1	1	1	1
2	2	2	2
3	3	3	3
4	4	4	4
5	5	5	5
6	6	6	6
7	7	7	7
8	8	8	8
9	9	9	9

13 THINK SOLVE EXPLAIN

Mark is saving money for a new portable media player. He saved $19 last month and $27 this month. How much more money does Mike need to buy the media player? Provide possible information needed to solve the problem. Then solve it. (1-5)

____

____

____

____

STOP

Name ______________________________

Mark the best answer.

1 If the money shown is to be divided among 5 people, what should be the first step? (2-3)

$50 $10 $10 $10 $10 $10

Ⓐ Exchange the $50 bill for two $20 bills and ten $1 bills.

Ⓑ Exchange the five $10 bills for fifty $1 bills.

Ⓒ Exchange the $50 bill for fifty $1 bills.

Ⓓ Exchange the $50 bill for five $10 bills.

2 Andrew used this model to divide. Which division sentence does his model show? (2-1)

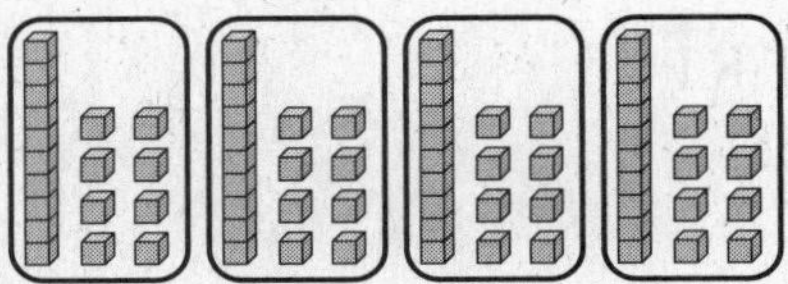

Ⓕ 70 ÷ 4 = 18

Ⓖ 72 ÷ 4 = 18

Ⓗ 74 ÷ 4 = 18

Ⓘ 78 ÷ 4 = 18

3 Six friends shared 363 stickers equally. What is 363 ÷ 6? (2-5)

Ⓐ 63

Ⓑ 61

Ⓒ 60 R3

Ⓓ 60 R1

4 Three friends earned $84 mowing lawns. If each friend earned the same amount of money, how much did each friend earn? (2-2)

Ⓕ $28

Ⓖ $24

Ⓗ $21

Ⓘ $20

5 The table shows the boxes of cookies sold by students as a school fundraiser. Marc sold 3 times as many boxes as Karen did. How many boxes of cookies did Karen sell? (2-5)

Student	Boxes
Marc	408
Karen	?
Mia	97

Ⓐ 204

Ⓑ 173

Ⓒ 136

Ⓓ 121

Go On

6 A teacher is making booklets of students' poems. She has to copy a total of 288 pages. Each booklet has 8 pages. Which of the following equations can be used to find n, the number of booklets she can make? (2-7)

288 pages

8 —— ***n* booklets** ——→

Pages per booklet

Ⓕ $288 \times 8 = n$

Ⓖ $288 \div 8 = n$

Ⓗ $288 - 8 = n$

Ⓘ $288 + 8 = n$

7 A summer camp has 110 campers divided as evenly as possible into 9 cabins. How many campers are in each cabin? (2-4)

Ⓐ There are 12 campers in each cabin, with 2 campers left.

Ⓑ There are 13 campers in each cabin.

Ⓒ There are 120 campers.

Ⓓ There are 11 campers in each cabin, with 2 campers left.

8 Kaylee solved the division problem $52 \div 7$ correctly. Which model did she use? (2-1)

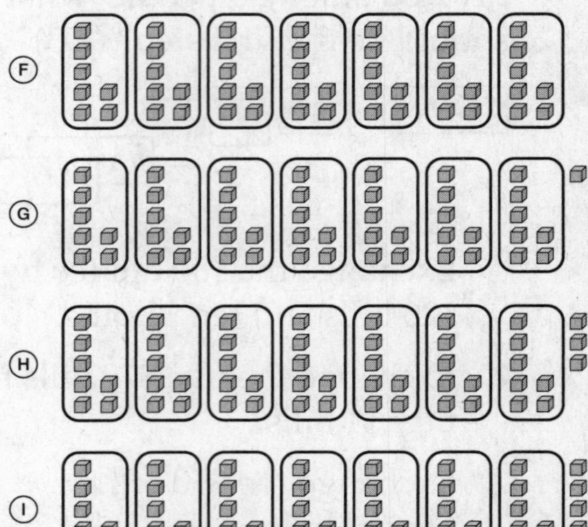

9 What is the quotient of $87 \div 4$? (2-2)

Ⓐ 22

Ⓑ 21 R3

Ⓒ 21 R1

Ⓓ 21

Go On

10 A gardener planted 105 sunflower seeds in 7 equal rows. Which of the following equations can be used to find *s*, the number of sunflower seeds in each row? (2-7)

105 sunflower seeds

s	s	s	s	s	s	s

↑Sunflower seeds in each row

Ⓕ $105 \times 7 = s$

Ⓖ $105 \div 7 = s$

Ⓗ $105 - 7 = s$

Ⓘ $105 + 7 = s$

11 During a sale, a department store sold 456 sweaters over 6 hours. If the store sold the same number of sweaters each hour, how many sweaters did it sell each hour? (2-4)

0	0	0	0
1	1	1	1
2	2	2	2
3	3	3	3
4	4	4	4
5	5	5	5
6	6	6	6
7	7	7	7
8	8	8	8
9	9	9	9

12 THINK SOLVE EXPLAIN A school spent $1,092 on 6 new microscopes for science classes. Each microscope cost an equal amount of money. Find the cost of 1 microscope. Show all of your work. (2-6)

____

____

____

____

____

STOP

Name ______________________

Mark the best answer.

1 A conference about healthy school lunches was held in Tampa, and 6,968 people attended. If each of Florida's 67 counties sent the same number of representatives, how many representatives were sent from each county? (3-6)

Ⓐ 104

Ⓑ 104 R3

Ⓒ 114 R34

Ⓓ 140

2 Which of the following is the best way to estimate 742 ÷ 81 using compatible numbers? (3-2)

Ⓕ 720 divided by 80

Ⓖ 745 divided by 85

Ⓗ 750 divided by 75

Ⓘ 750 divided by 90

3 Joaquin is baking cookies for his class. Each cookie sheet can hold 12 cookies and he bakes 11 sheets of cookies. If there is a total of 44 students in his class, which of the following can be used to find out how many cookies each student will get? (3-8)

Ⓐ $11 \times 12 - 44 = 88$ cookies

Ⓑ $11 \times 12 \div 44 = 3$ cookies

Ⓒ $44 + 11 \div 12 = 40$ cookies

Ⓓ $44 \div 11 + 12 = 16$ cookies

4 A florist has ordered 632 roses. If the roses are divided into 50 bouquets how many roses will each bouquet have, and how many roses will be left over? (3-3)

Ⓕ 12 per bouquet with none left over.

Ⓖ 13 per bouquet with 3 left over.

Ⓗ 13 per bouquet with 32 left over.

Ⓘ 12 per bouquet with 32 left over.

5 Which of the following is another way to think of 46,000 ÷ 70? (3-1)

Ⓐ 46,000 tens ÷ 70 tens

Ⓑ 4,600 tens ÷ 7 tens

Ⓒ 460 tens ÷ 7 tens

Ⓓ 46 tens ÷ 7 tens

6 A fund has $10,752 available for scholarships. If 42 students are awarded equal scholarships from the fund, how much does each student receive? (3-7)

Ⓕ $125

Ⓖ $255

Ⓗ $256

Ⓘ $264

Go On

7 How many tables that seat eight are required to provide places for 62 people at a banquet? (3-4)

Ⓐ 9

Ⓑ 8

Ⓒ 7

Ⓓ 6

8 Dave needs to buy 104 bagels for the company meeting. According to the prices shown, how much would he save if he bought them by the baker's dozen instead of buying them separately? (3-8)

Bagel Prices	
One Bagel	$2
Baker's Dozen (13 per dozen)	$11

Ⓕ $9

Ⓖ $88

Ⓗ $112

Ⓘ $120

9 A ream of paper contains 500 sheets. How many reams are needed to type a manuscript of 6,000 pages? (3-3)

Ⓐ 12

Ⓑ 30

Ⓒ 120

Ⓓ 300

10 The amounts two friends earned at their yard sales are given in the table. About how many times as much did Chen earn than Bianca? (3-2)

Amount Earned	
Bianca	$26
Chen	$132

Ⓕ 13

Ⓖ 7

Ⓗ 5

Ⓘ 2

11 A company printed 232 brochures and shipped them out in boxes. If there were 58 brochures in each box, how many boxes were shipped? (3-4)

Ⓐ 7

Ⓑ 5

Ⓒ 4

Ⓓ 3

12 A group of 11 friends rents a van to take a summer road trip. If they drive a total of 1,320 miles and each person drives an equal amount of miles, how many miles will each person drive? (3-5)

Ⓕ 120 miles

Ⓖ 150 miles

Ⓗ 175 miles

Ⓘ 193 miles

Name ______________________________

13 The ruby-throated hummingbird is the most common hummingbird in Florida. During 15 minutes of flight, the hummingbird's heart will beat 18,300 times, on average. How many times will it beat per minute? (3-7)

Ⓐ 122

Ⓑ 305

Ⓒ 1,200 R3

Ⓓ 1,220

14 We Haul trucking company purchased 36,000 boxes. If 90 boxes can fit on a truck, how many trucks will be needed to carry all the boxes? (3-1)

0	0	0	0
1	1	1	1
2	2	2	2
3	3	3	3
4	4	4	4
5	5	5	5
6	6	6	6
7	7	7	7
8	8	8	8
9	9	9	9

15 THINK SOLVE EXPLAIN

Chelle will be marching in the parade. Chelle knows the parade route is exactly 1,582 yards long. Every 25 yards, she has to toss her baton in the air. How many times will Chelle toss her baton? Explain your answer. (3-5)

____

____

____

____

____

____

____

____

____

STOP

Name ______________________

Mark the best answer.

1 Which of the following is equal to 3^4? (4-1)

Ⓐ 3×4

Ⓑ $4 \times 4 \times 4$

Ⓒ $3 \times 3 \times 3 \times 3$

Ⓓ $3 \times 4 \times 3 \times 4$

2 What is the first step in simplifying the expression below? (4-2)

$15 \times 3 - 2 + 4^3$

Ⓕ Multiply 15 by 3.

Ⓖ Add 2 and 4^3.

Ⓗ Simplify 4^3.

Ⓘ Subtract 2 from 3.

3 There is a $100 equipment fee plus a cost of $50 a day for each student who attends a sports camp. The total cost for a student to attend is $100 + 50n$, where n is the number of days. Evaluate $100 + 50n$ if $n = 4$. (4-3)

Ⓐ $100

Ⓑ $200

Ⓒ $300

Ⓓ $400

4 Ferdinand has 125 minutes of recess every school week. The number of minutes for each recess can be found by solving the equation $5m = 125$. What is the value of m? (4-6)

Ⓕ $m = 25$

Ⓖ $m = 30$

Ⓗ $m = 120$

Ⓘ $m = 130$

5 What step can be taken to get the x by itself on one side in the equation $x + 18 = 50$? (4-5)

Ⓐ Multiply both sides of the equation by 18.

Ⓑ Divide both sides of the equation by 18.

Ⓒ Add 18 to both sides of the equation.

Ⓓ Subtract 18 from both sides of the equation.

6 There are 43 bicycles in a bicycle shop. The number of silver bicycles is 13. The number of red bicycles is 4 times as great as the number of black bicycles. How many red bicycles are in the bicycle shop? (4-4)

Ⓕ 30

Ⓖ 24

Ⓗ 13

Ⓘ 6

7 A clothing store has 3 black sweatshirts and 4 racks of white sweatshirts with the same number of sweatshirts on each rack. The total number of sweatshirts can be found by evaluating the expression $3 + 4s$. If $s = 5$, what is the value of $3 + 4s$? (4-3)

Ⓐ 7

Ⓑ 12

Ⓒ 20

Ⓓ 23

8 Which of the following expressions has a value of 16? (4-2)

Ⓕ $18 + 12 \div 3 \times 2$

Ⓖ $(18 - 12) \div 3 \times 2$

Ⓗ $18 - 12 \div (3 \times 2)$

Ⓘ $18 - (12 \div 3) \times 2$

9 Margo has 15 foreign coins, which is 5 fewer than the number Amanze has. The number of foreign coins that Amanze has can be found by solving the equation $x - 5 = 15$. What is the value of x? (4-5)

Ⓐ $x = 20$

Ⓑ $x = 10$

Ⓒ $x = 5$

Ⓓ $x = 12$

10 What step can be taken to get the variable w alone on one side of the equation $6w = 42$? (4-6)

Ⓕ Add 6 to both sides of the equation.

Ⓖ Subtract 6 from both sides of the equation.

Ⓗ Multiply both sides of the equation by 6.

Ⓘ Divide both sides of the equation by 6.

11 A zoo is open for 6 hours on Friday and 3 more hours on Saturday than Sunday. The zoo is open for a total of 19 hours on Friday, Saturday, and Sunday. How many hours is the zoo open on Sunday? (4-4)

Ⓐ 5 hours

Ⓑ 6 hours

Ⓒ 8 hours

Ⓓ 24 hours

Go On

Name ______________________

12 At a carwash, students earned a total of \$240. The total was divided equally among 4 fifth-grade classes. Which equation can be used to find n, the amount each class received? (4-7)

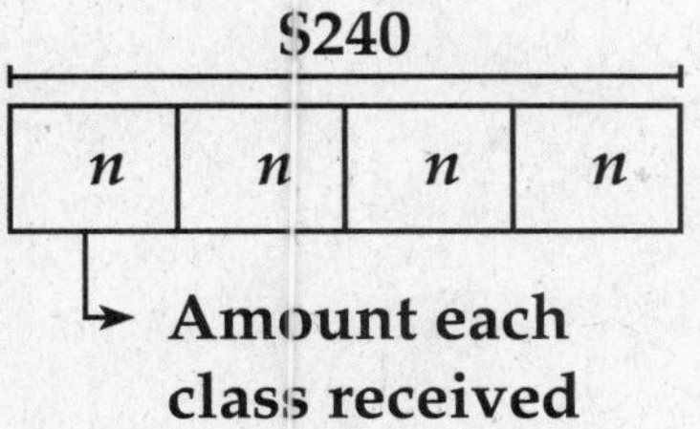

Ⓕ $n + 4 = 240$

Ⓖ $n - 4 = 240$

Ⓗ $n \div 4 = 240$

Ⓘ $n \times 4 = 240$

13 The number of square tiles on a kitchen floor is 12^2. What is the standard form of 12^2? (4-1)

0	0	0	0
1	1	1	1
2	2	2	2
3	3	3	3
4	4	4	4
5	5	5	5
6	6	6	6
7	7	7	7
8	8	8	8
9	9	9	9

14 THINK SOLVE EXPLAIN

Mrs. Bell needs to make 60 vests for the winter concert. She plans to make an equal number of vests each week for 5 weeks. Draw a picture. Then write and solve an equation to find the number of vests she will make each week. (4-7)

____

____

____

____

STOP

Name ______________________

1 Which of the following is a method for finding the quotient of 360 ÷ 9?

Ⓐ You know 9 × 4 = 36, so 360 ÷ 9 = 4.

Ⓑ Multiply 9 by 36 and insert one zero on the end of the product.

Ⓒ You know 9 × 4 = 36, so 36 ÷ 9 = 4 and 360 ÷ 9 = 40.

Ⓓ Divide 360 by 9 and multiply by 36.

2 Jamie rode his bike 165 miles in 5 days. He rode the same number of miles each day. To find how many miles he rode each day, how can you break down the dividend using place value and then divide?

Ⓕ (100 + 60 + 5) ÷ 5

Ⓖ (10 + 60 + 5) ÷ 5

Ⓗ (155 + 10) ÷ 5

Ⓘ (90 + 75) ÷ 5

3 Which division sentence does the model show?

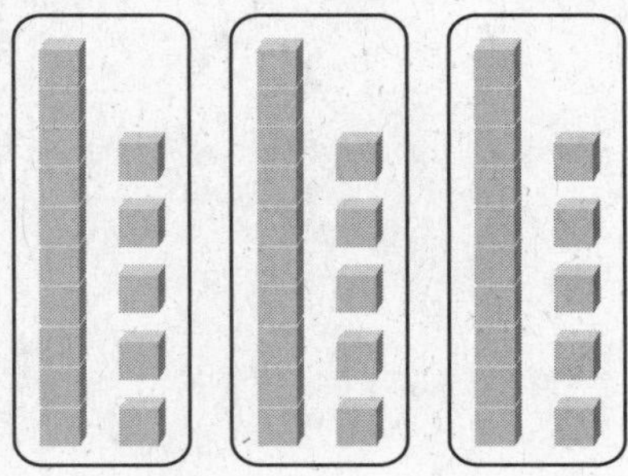

Ⓐ 45 ÷ 3 = 15

Ⓑ 45 ÷ 5 = 9

Ⓒ 34 ÷ 3 = 15

Ⓓ 3 × 15 = 45

4 What is the next step in dividing the money shown below evenly among 5 people?

Ⓕ Exchange a $100 bill for 100 $1 bills.

Ⓖ Exchange all $100 bills for $10 bills.

Ⓗ Share the $10 bills.

Ⓘ Exchange all $100 bills for $5 bills.

5 Mr. Henderson sold 42 oranges. If each customer purchased 3 oranges, which picture and equation can be used to find the number of customers that purchased oranges?

Ⓐ 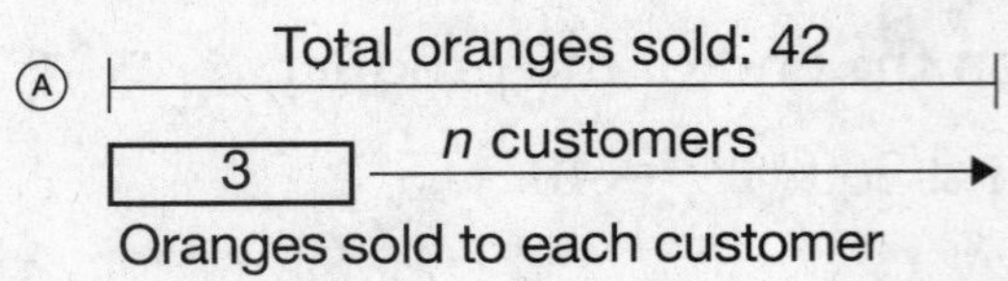

$42 \div 3 = n$

Ⓑ Oranges sold to each customer: 3

42 | *n* customers →

Total oranges sold: 42

$3 \div 42 = n$

Ⓒ Total oranges sold: 42

14	14	14

Oranges sold to each customer

$14 + 14 + 14 = n$

Ⓓ Oranges sold to each customer: *n*

42 | 3 customers →

Total oranges sold

$n \div 42 = 3$

6 What is the quotient of $180 \div 9$?

7 Rachel has 221 cans of fruit to stack on 7 shelves. Which is the best estimate for the number of cans that will fit on one shelf?

Ⓕ 20

Ⓖ 30

Ⓗ 35

Ⓘ 45

Go On

8 Ryan divided 626 by 7. He said the quotient is 89 R3. Which is the best estimate Ryan can use to check to see if his answer is reasonable?

Ⓐ 630 ÷ 10 = 63

Ⓑ 560 ÷ 7 = 80

Ⓒ 630 ÷ 7 = 90

Ⓓ 700 ÷ 7 = 100

9 Which of the following is another way to think of 20,000 ÷ 40?

Ⓕ 2,000 tens ÷ 4 tens

Ⓖ 2,000 tens ÷ 40 tens

Ⓗ 200 tens ÷ 4 tens

Ⓘ 200 tens ÷ 40 tens

10 The distance between Ames Research Center in California and Kennedy Space Center in Florida is about 2,457 miles. To estimate the number of hours it would take to drive the distance at 58 miles per hour, which are the best compatible numbers to use?

Ⓐ 2,457 ÷ 60

Ⓑ 2,000 ÷ 50

Ⓒ 2,400 ÷ 80

Ⓓ 2,400 ÷ 60

11 Binh is sharing 28 orange slices with 2 other people. If the 3 people had an equal number of slices, how many slices did each person have? How many slices are left?

Ⓕ Each person had 9 slices with 1 slice left.

Ⓖ Each person had 8 slices with 5 slices left.

Ⓗ Each person had 7 slices with 6 slices left.

Ⓘ Each person had 6 slices with 9 slices left.

Go On

Name ______________________________

12 Michelle has 84 game pieces. Each game needs 9 pieces. Michelle says she has enough pieces for 9 games. Is her answer reasonable?

Ⓐ No. She has enough pieces left over for another game.

Ⓑ No. She has only has enough pieces for 8 games.

Ⓒ Yes, her answer is reasonable.

Ⓓ No, there is not enough information to determine if her answer is reasonable.

13 How much money will 4 people get if $96 is divided equally among them?

Ⓕ $30

Ⓖ $25

Ⓗ $24

Ⓘ $14

14 Julius was asked to divide 743 marbles equally into 4 bags. How many marbles will be in each bag?

Ⓐ 184 with 3 left over

Ⓑ 184 with 7 left over

Ⓒ 184

Ⓓ 185 with 3 left over

15 The school sports center has 535 seats. There are 5 sections and each section has the same number of seats. How many seats are in each section?

Ⓕ 170

Ⓖ 107

Ⓗ 101

Ⓘ 17

Go On

Name ______________________

16 A school ordered 576 pads of paper. If each of 20 classes receive the same number of pads of paper, how many pads of paper will each class receive?

Ⓐ 28 with 16 pads left over

Ⓑ 29

Ⓒ 29 with 16 pads left over

Ⓓ 30 with 8 pads left over

17 In the past 31 days, Jeremy received 248 new emails. Each day, he received the same number of emails. How many emails did Jeremy receive each day?

18 Each row in the auditorium has 18 seats. If 246 students and teachers are going to watch an assembly in the auditorium, how many rows of seats are needed to seat everyone?

Ⓕ 13 rows

Ⓖ 14 rows

Ⓗ 15 rows

Ⓘ 16 rows

Go On

19 THINK SOLVE EXPLAIN A group of band members will be performing along the 119 miles from Kissimmee to Sarasota to raise money for uniforms. If they perform every 25 miles as they travel this distance, how many performances will they give? Explain.

____

____

____

____

____

20 The odometer on Kate's car read 42,368 miles. On average, Kate's car can get 32 miles per gallon of gas. How many gallons of gas has Kate used so far to travel these miles?

Ⓐ 1,320

Ⓑ 1,324

Ⓒ 1,330

Ⓓ 1,336

21 Since 1947 Everglades National Park has grown from 460,000 acres to 1,509,000 acres. Which equation can be solved to find n, the number of acres the park has increased since 1947?

Ⓕ $460{,}000 \div n = 1{,}509{,}000$

Ⓖ $460{,}000 - n = 1{,}509{,}000$

Ⓗ $460{,}000 \times n = 1{,}509{,}000$

Ⓘ $460{,}000 + n = 1{,}509{,}000$

22 Marissa has 16 stickers in an album. She has 4 stickers on each page. Which equation gives the number of pages with stickers on them?

Ⓐ $n - 4 = 16$

Ⓑ $\frac{n}{16} = 4$

Ⓒ $4n = 16$

Ⓓ $4 + n = 16$

Go On

23 Josh has 79 role-playing cards. He separated them into 3 different stacks. The first stack has 19 cards, the second stack has 25 cards, and the third stack has the remaining cards. Josh wants to find how many cards are in the third stack. Which picture and equation represents the problem?

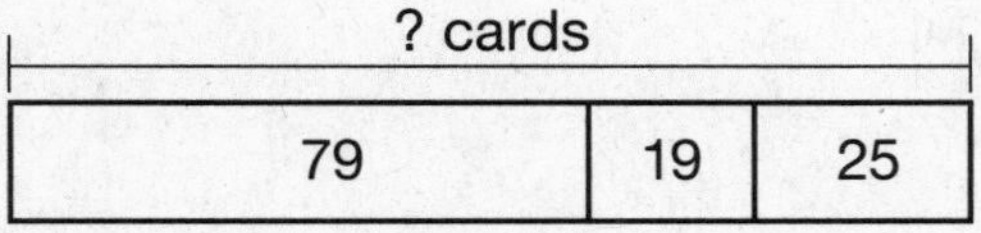

Ⓕ ? cards

79	19	25

$n = 79 + 19 + 25$

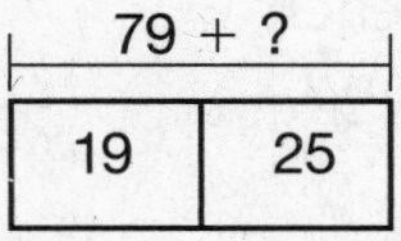

Ⓖ 79 + ?

19	25

$79 + n = 9 + 25$

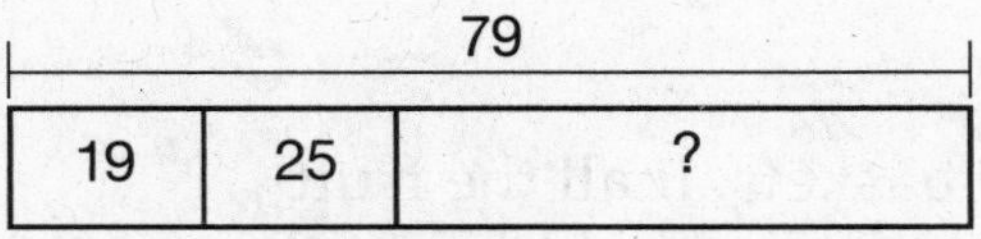

Ⓗ 79

19	25	?

$19 + 25 + n = 79$

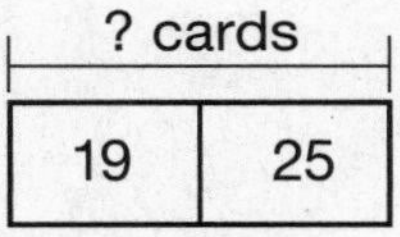

Ⓘ ? cards

19	25

$n = 19 + 25$

24 Which of the following is equal to 3^4?

Ⓐ $3 \times 3 \times 3 \times 3$

Ⓑ $3 \times 3 \times 3$

Ⓒ $4 \times 4 \times 4$

Ⓓ 3×4

25 Which expression has a value of 36?

Ⓕ $6 + (5 \times 5)$

Ⓖ $(3 \times 5) + (8 + 8)$

Ⓗ $(42 \div 7) + (25 - 10)$

Ⓘ $3^3 + (19 - 10)$

Go On

Name ______________________________

26 Marcus has 16 books. Jerome has 8 more books than Marcus. Evaluate the expression $m + 8$ for $m = 16$. How many books does Jerome have?

Ⓐ 128

Ⓑ 24

Ⓒ 8

Ⓓ 2

27 A walkway is made up of 736 bricks. There are 8 bricks in each row of the walkway. There are 450 red bricks in the walkway. How many rows of bricks does the walkway contain?

Ⓕ 92 Ⓗ 96

Ⓖ 94 Ⓘ 98

28 There are 30 pieces of fruit in each of 10 baskets. If all the fruit is to be divided equally among 5 groups of people, which of the following shows how many pieces of fruit each group will get?

Ⓐ $30 \times 5 - 10 = 140$

Ⓑ $30 \times 5 \div 10 = 15$

Ⓒ $30 \times 10 \div 5 = 60$

Ⓓ $30 + 10 \div 5 = 8$

29 THINK SOLVE EXPLAIN

Each of 56 students chose one snack from the following: pretzels, popcorn, or trail mix. There were 9 students who choose trail mix. The number of students who choose popcorn is 2 times the number who chose trail mix. How many of each kind of snack were chosen by the students?

____

____

____

____

____

STOP

Name ______________________

Mark the best answer.

Use the coordinate grid below for Questions **1** through **4**.

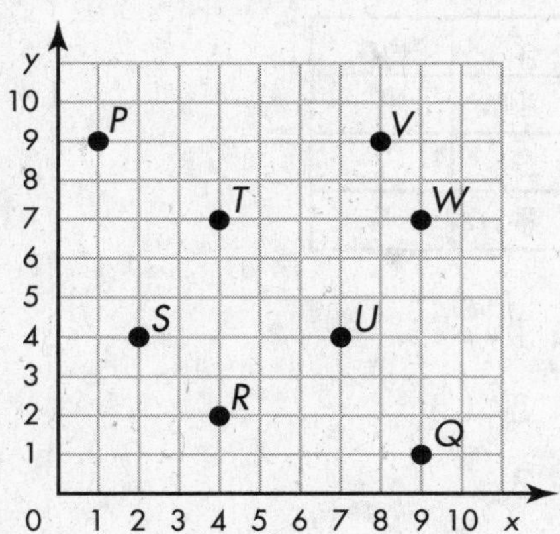

1 Which point is located at (9, 1)? (5-1)

Ⓐ *P*

Ⓑ *Q*

Ⓒ *V*

Ⓓ *R*

2 What is the ordered pair for Point *U*? (5-1)

Ⓕ (7, 9)

Ⓖ (9, 7)

Ⓗ (4, 7)

Ⓘ (7, 4)

3 What is the vertical distance between Point *T* and Point *R*? (5-2)

Ⓐ 7 units

Ⓑ 6 units

Ⓒ 4 units

Ⓓ 5 units

4 Which tells how to find the horizontal distance between Point *T* and Point *W*? (5-2)

Ⓕ Subtract 9 – 4

Ⓖ Subtract 9 – 7

Ⓗ Subtract 7 – 4

Ⓘ Subtract 7 – 1

Use the simple map below for Questions **5** and **6**.

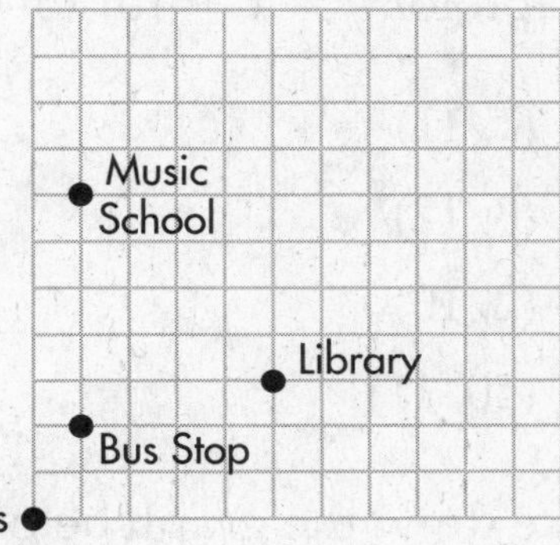

5 How many total blocks does Celia need to walk north and east to get from her home to the library? (5-3)

Ⓐ 6

Ⓑ 7

Ⓒ 8

Ⓓ 9

Go On

6 Celia is at the bus stop. She decided to walk to the library and then to the music school. How many blocks did Celia walk? (5-3)

Ⓕ 5

Ⓖ 7

Ⓗ 8

Ⓘ 13

7 Which ordered pair is on the graph for $y = x + 10$? (5-4)

Ⓐ (1, 11)

Ⓑ (3, 12)

Ⓒ (2, 10)

Ⓓ (10, 11)

8 Jake drew the graph below. Which equation did he graph? (5-4)

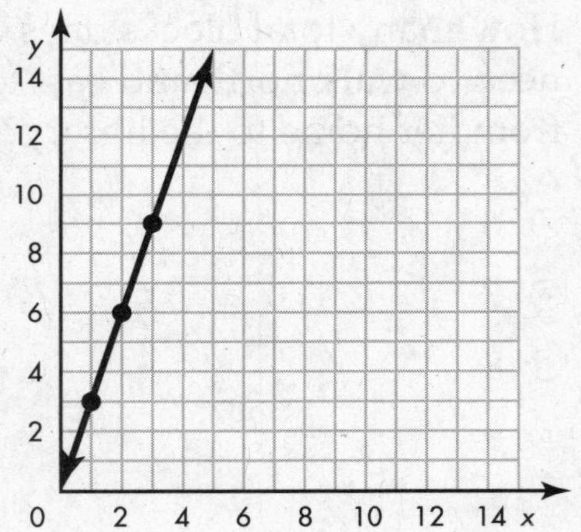

Ⓕ $y = 2x$

Ⓖ $y = 3x$

Ⓗ $y = x + 2$

Ⓘ $y = x + 3$

9 Which number completes the table of values for $y = 7x \div 7$? (5-5)

x	y
1	1
3	?
5	5

Ⓐ 1

Ⓑ 2

Ⓒ 3

Ⓓ 4

10 Which ordered pair is on the graph of the equation below? (5-5)

$y = 3x + 6$

Ⓕ (2, 10)

Ⓖ (2, 11)

Ⓗ (2, 12)

Ⓘ (2, 13)

Go On

Name ____________________

11 From the library, Sean walked 4 blocks east, 2 blocks north, 2 blocks west, and 2 blocks south. How many blocks was he from the library? (5-3)

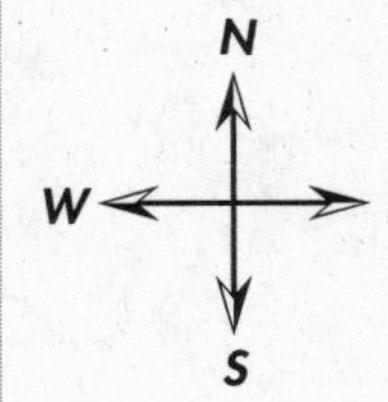

12 

The graph shows the time, in seconds, it takes a baby to walk a distance in feet from a sofa in the early stages of walking. Write a short description of the baby's progress from Point *A* to Point *F*. (5-6)

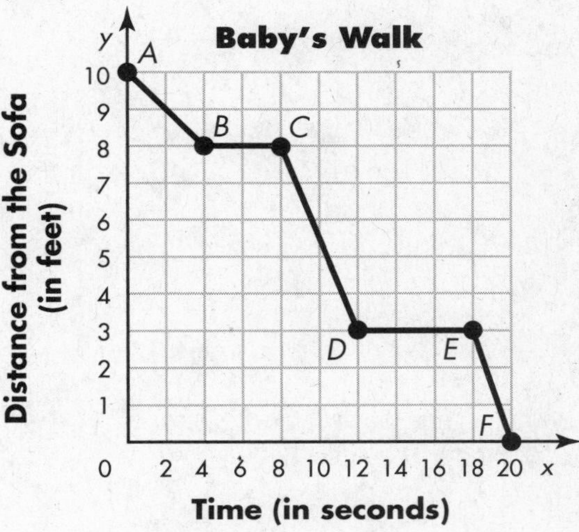

____

____

____

____

____

____

____

____

____

STOP

Name ______________________

1 What is 3.962 rounded to the nearest hundredth? (6-1)

Ⓐ 3.90

Ⓑ 3.95

Ⓒ 3.96

Ⓓ 3.97

2 What is 12.8094 rounded to the nearest whole number? (6-1)

Ⓕ 12

Ⓖ 12.8

Ⓗ 13

Ⓘ 13.8

3 What missing decimal goes in square *Y* of the decimal place value chart? (6-2)

0.55	0.56	0.57		
0.65		0.67	0.68	*Y*
0.75			0.78	0.79

Ⓐ 0.6

Ⓑ 0.69

Ⓒ 0.7

Ⓓ 0.77

4 Roger's kite is 48.15 centimeters long. Mary's kite is 46.817 centimeters long. Which is the best estimate of the difference between the two measures? (6-3)

Ⓕ 1 centimeter

Ⓖ 2 centimeters

Ⓗ 4 centimeters

Ⓘ 6 centimeters

5 On Saturday, Walter walked his dog 5.83 kilometers. Then he walked 3.42 kilometers to the store. Which is the best estimate of the total number of kilometers Walter walked? (6-3)

Ⓐ 10 kilometers

Ⓑ 9 kilometers

Ⓒ 8 kilometers

Ⓓ 3 kilometers

6 Mitch bought a red marker for $0.68 and a notebook for $1.29. What was the total amount he spent? (6-4)

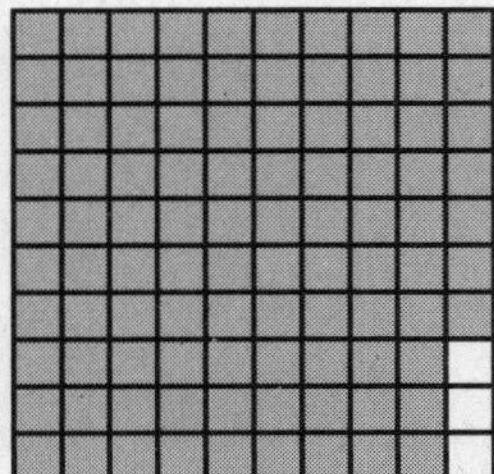

Ⓕ $0.61

Ⓖ $1.77

Ⓗ $1.87

Ⓘ $1.97

7 Jasmine is using place-value blocks to add 7.39 + 3.65. Which describes the *last* step in solving the problem? (6-5)

Ⓐ Add 7 + 3 + 1

Ⓑ Add 9 hundredths + 5 hundredths

Ⓒ Regroup 10 hundredths as 1 tenth

Ⓓ Add 3 tenths + 6 tenths

8 Filipe needs to run two miles for soccer team try-outs. He ran his first mile in 10.18 minutes. He ran his second mile in 10.56 minutes. What is Filipe's combined time for the two miles? (6-7)

Ⓕ 20.64 minutes

Ⓖ 20.74 minutes

Ⓗ 20.84 minutes

Ⓘ 21.74 minutes

9 Tamara buys a shirt for $14.69 and a pair of pants for $21.32. How much more does she spend for the pants than for the shirt? (6-8)

Ⓐ $2.73

Ⓑ $6.28

Ⓒ $6.49

Ⓓ $6.63

10 Manny's batting average in 2008 was .321, and Jason's was .238. How much greater was Manny's batting average than Jason's? (6-8)

Ⓕ .093

Ⓖ .083

Ⓗ .073

Ⓘ .063

11 The Ming family spent $15 on lunch and $7 on dessert. Which is a way to find how much change they would get from $30? (6-10)

Ⓐ Subtract the sum of 15 and 7 from 30

Ⓑ Subtract 15 from the sum of 7 and 30

Ⓒ Add 30 to the difference of 15 and 7

Ⓓ Add 7 to the difference of 30 and 15

Go On

Name ______________________________

12 Meera's goal for the weekend is to spend 9 hours preparing for the school play. On Saturday, she spent 3 hours reading her lines and 1.5 hours on her costume. How many more hours should Meera spend preparing for the play in order to meet her goal? (6-10)

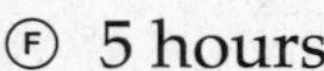

Ⓕ 5 hours

Ⓖ 4.75 hours

Ⓗ 4.5 hours

Ⓘ 4.25 hours

13 What is 5.96 + 8.34 − 4.96? (6-9)

$			.		
	0	0		0	0
	1	1		1	1
	2	2		2	2
	3	3		3	3
	4	4		4	4
	5	5		5	5
	6	6		6	6
	7	7		7	7
	8	8		8	8
	9	9		9	9

14 

THINK SOLVE EXPLAIN

Wilbur is using place-value blocks to subtract 2.64 − 1.59. Explain how he can use the place-value model below to find the difference. (6-6)

STOP

Name ______________________________

1 What is the prime factorization of 24? (7-3)

Ⓐ $4 \times 4 \times 4 \times 6 = 4^3 \times 6$

Ⓑ $2 \times 3 \times 4 \times 8$

Ⓒ $2 \times 2 \times 3 \times 4 = 2^2 \times 3 \times 4$

Ⓓ $2 \times 2 \times 2 \times 3 = 2^3 \times 3$

2 On Tuesday, $\frac{2}{9}$ of the students in a class wore jeans. What fraction of the class did NOT wear jeans? (7-8)

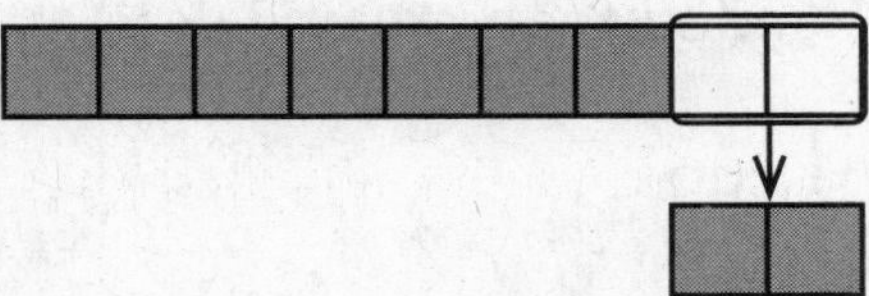

Ⓕ $\frac{9}{9}$

Ⓖ $\frac{7}{9}$

Ⓗ $\frac{5}{7}$

Ⓘ $\frac{2}{7}$

3 Milos and Asha are doing their homework. Milos has finished $\frac{3}{6}$ of his. Asha has finished $\frac{1}{6}$ of hers. How much more homework has Milos finished than Asha? (7-9)

Ⓐ $\frac{3}{6} - \frac{1}{6} = \frac{2}{6} = \frac{1}{3}$

Ⓑ $\frac{3}{6} - \frac{1}{6} = \frac{2}{0}$

Ⓒ $\frac{3}{6} + \frac{1}{6} = \frac{4}{6} = \frac{2}{3}$

Ⓓ $\frac{3}{6} + \frac{1}{6} = \frac{4}{12} = \frac{1}{3}$

4 Which of the numbers below is an example of a prime number? (7-2)

Ⓕ 12

Ⓖ 18

Ⓗ 23

Ⓘ 32

5 Which equation is represented on the number line shown? (7-10)

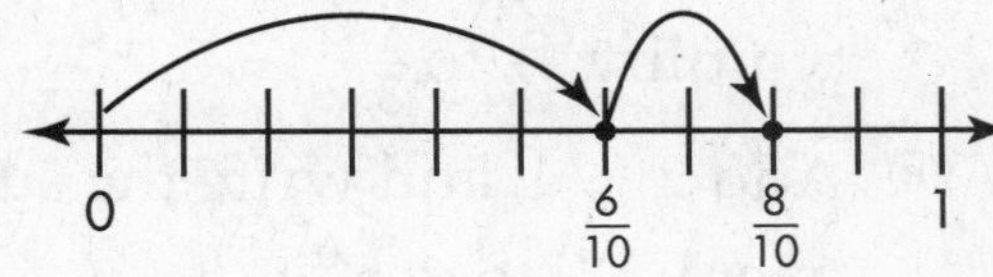

Ⓐ $\frac{6}{6} + \frac{2}{2} = \frac{8}{8}$

Ⓑ $\frac{10}{10} - \frac{6}{10} = \frac{4}{10} = \frac{2}{5}$

Ⓒ $\frac{6}{10} + \frac{2}{10} = \frac{8}{20}$

Ⓓ $\frac{6}{10} + \frac{2}{10} = \frac{8}{10} = \frac{4}{5}$

Go On

Name ______________________________

6 Edna has $\frac{2}{9}$ foot of purple ribbon and $\frac{4}{9}$ foot of yellow ribbon. Which of the following can be used to find how much ribbon she has in all? (7-7)

Ⓕ Add 2 + 4, and write the sum over 9 to get $\frac{6}{9}$. Simplify $\frac{6}{9}$ to $\frac{2}{3}$.

Ⓖ Add 2 + 4, and write the sum over 9 + 9 to get $\frac{6}{18}$. Simplify $\frac{6}{18}$ to $\frac{1}{3}$.

Ⓗ Add 2 + 4, and write the sum over 9 − 9 to get $\frac{6}{0}$.

Ⓘ Add 9 + 9, and write the sum over 2 + 4 to get $\frac{18}{6}$. Simplify $\frac{18}{6}$ to 3.

7 The table shows the different colors of kittens at an animal shelter. In simplest form, what fraction of kittens are orange tabbies? (7-5)

Color of Kittens	Number of Kittens
Black & White	11
Gray Stripes	4
Orange Tabby	6

Ⓐ $\frac{2}{7}$

Ⓑ $\frac{3}{7}$

Ⓒ $\frac{1}{2}$

Ⓓ $\frac{2}{3}$

8 What is the greatest common factor of 36 and 60? (7-4)

Ⓕ 20

Ⓖ 18

Ⓗ 15

Ⓘ 12

9 A soup recipe calls for $\frac{7}{8}$ cup of chicken broth and $\frac{3}{8}$ cup of cream. How much more chicken broth is needed than cream? (7-9)

Ⓐ $\frac{1}{2}$ cup

Ⓑ $\frac{2}{3}$ cup

Ⓒ $\frac{5}{8}$ cup

Ⓓ $\frac{1}{8}$ cup

10 Katerina is knitting a scarf. She knit $\frac{4}{9}$ of the scarf on Monday and $\frac{2}{9}$ of the scarf on Tuesday. What fraction of the scarf has she knit? (7-6)

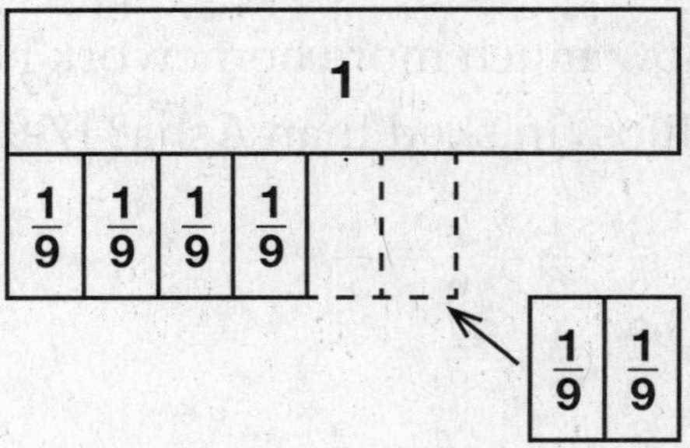

Ⓕ $\frac{2}{9}$

Ⓖ $\frac{1}{3}$

Ⓗ $\frac{1}{2}$

Ⓘ $\frac{2}{3}$

Name ______________________________

11 What number has only 1, 3, 9, and 27 as its factors? (7-1)

0	0	0	0
1	1	1	1
2	2	2	2
3	3	3	3
4	4	4	4
5	5	5	5
6	6	6	6
7	7	7	7
8	8	8	8
9	9	9	9

12 Meenah made a conjecture that any even number will be divisible by 4. Test her conjecture. Explain whether it is correct or incorrect. (7-11)

____

____

____

____

____

____

____

STOP

Name ______________________________

Topic 8
Florida Test

Mark the best answer.

1 Ms. Levitt put a $\frac{1}{3}$-pound box on a scale and a $\frac{5}{6}$-pound rock on the same scale. Which picture matches an equation you could solve to find the total weight of the two items on the scale? (8-7)

Ⓐ
$\frac{1}{3}$

$\frac{5}{6}$	x

Ⓑ
$\frac{1}{3}$

$\frac{5}{6}$	$\frac{5}{6}$	x

Ⓒ
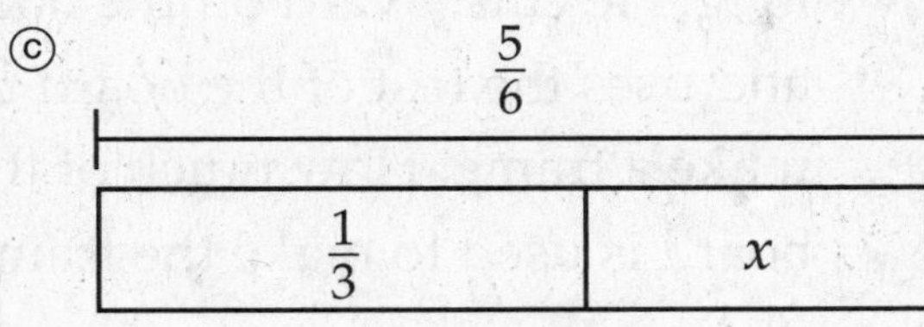

Ⓓ
x

$\frac{1}{3}$	$\frac{5}{6}$

2 Replace each addend with 0, $\frac{1}{2}$, or 1. What is the best estimate of the sum of $\frac{5}{12} + \frac{5}{9}$? (8-5)

Ⓕ $\frac{1}{2} + 1 = 1\frac{1}{2}$

Ⓖ $0 + 1 = 1$

Ⓗ $\frac{1}{2} + \frac{1}{2} = 1$

Ⓘ $1 + 1 = 2$

3 Which of the following pairs of numbers has a least common multiple of 36? (8-1)

Ⓐ 3 and 12

Ⓑ 2 and 18

Ⓒ 4 and 9

Ⓓ 6 and 8

4 At a fair, Katie sells $\frac{1}{6}$ of the total balloons and Jacob sells $\frac{3}{4}$ of the total balloons. What fraction represents the total amount of balloons sold? (8-3)

Ⓕ $\frac{1}{6}$

Ⓖ $\frac{2}{5}$

Ⓗ $\frac{3}{4}$

Ⓘ $\frac{11}{12}$

5 If hot dogs come in packages of 6 and hot-dog buns come in packages of 8, what is the least number of hot dogs and buns you could buy to have the same number of hot dogs and buns? (8-1)

Ⓐ 18

Ⓑ 24

Ⓒ 36

Ⓓ 48

Go On

6 Which renames $\frac{5}{8}$ and $\frac{3}{6}$ using a common denominator? (8-2)

Ⓕ $\frac{5}{24}$ and $\frac{3}{24}$
Ⓖ $\frac{15}{24}$ and $\frac{12}{24}$
Ⓗ $\frac{15}{24}$ and $\frac{9}{24}$
Ⓘ $\frac{20}{24}$ and $\frac{12}{24}$

7 Mineko had a piece of material that was $\frac{3}{5}$ yard long. She cut $\frac{1}{3}$ yard off the material to make a pillow. How much material does she have left? (8-4)

Ⓐ $\frac{1}{3}$ yard
Ⓑ $\frac{4}{15}$ yard
Ⓒ $\frac{1}{5}$ yard
Ⓓ $\frac{1}{15}$ yard

8 Which of the following is NOT a common denominator for $\frac{1}{4}$ and $\frac{5}{8}$? (8-2)

Ⓕ 32
Ⓖ 24
Ⓗ 8
Ⓘ 12

9 Maria spent 15 minutes, or $\frac{1}{4}$ hour, having breakfast. She spent 40 minutes, or $\frac{2}{3}$ hour having lunch. In simplest form, what fraction of an hour did Maria spend eating breakfast and lunch? (8-6)

Ⓐ $\frac{1}{4}$
Ⓑ $\frac{3}{7}$
Ⓒ $\frac{3}{4}$
Ⓓ $\frac{11}{12}$

10 Rodney has a board that is $\frac{5}{6}$ yard long. He cuts $\frac{1}{5}$ yard off the board and uses the rest of the board to make a frame. How much of the board is used to make the frame? (8-4)

Ⓕ $\frac{1}{12}$ yard
Ⓖ $\frac{1}{6}$ yard
Ⓗ $\frac{1}{3}$ yard
Ⓘ $\frac{19}{30}$ yard

Go On

11 Of the figures shown, $\frac{1}{4}$ are triangles and $\frac{1}{12}$ are arrows. What fraction of the figures are either arrows or triangles? (8-3)

Ⓐ $\frac{1}{3}$

Ⓑ $\frac{1}{4}$

Ⓒ $\frac{1}{12}$

Ⓓ $\frac{1}{24}$

12 Katie and her brother are both writing a report. Katie wrote $\frac{7}{8}$ of her report and her brother wrote $\frac{3}{7}$ of his report. What is the best estimate of how much more Katie wrote than her brother? (8-5)

Ⓕ $\frac{1}{2} - 0 = \frac{1}{2}$

Ⓖ $\frac{1}{2} - \frac{1}{2} = 0$

Ⓗ $1 - \frac{1}{2} = \frac{1}{2}$

Ⓘ $1 - 0 = 1$

13 What number is the least common multiple of 6 and 20? (8-1)

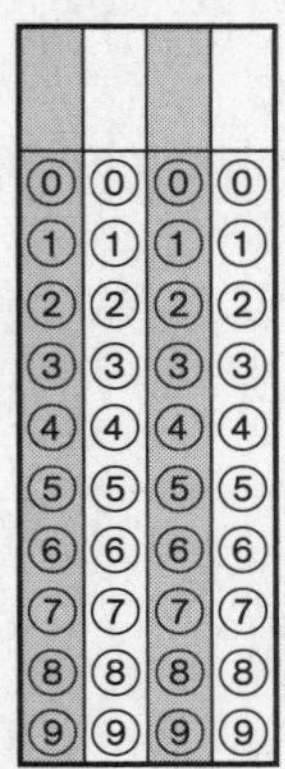

14 THINK SOLVE EXPLAIN Dena is biking down a $\frac{9}{10}$-mile bike trail. She stops to greet a friend after biking $\frac{1}{3}$ of a mile. How much farther does she need to travel? Draw a picture and write an equation to solve. (8-7)

____

____

STOP

Name ______________________________________

1 A 9-foot-tall palm tree was planted and grew 2 feet each year for n years. Which expression could be used to find how tall the tree is after growing for n years?

Ⓐ $9 + 2 \times n$

Ⓑ $9 \times (2 \times n)$

Ⓒ $9 + 2 + n$

Ⓓ $(9 \times 2) + n$

2 Lavon saves $1 every week from the money he earns doing chores. He drew the graph below to show his savings.

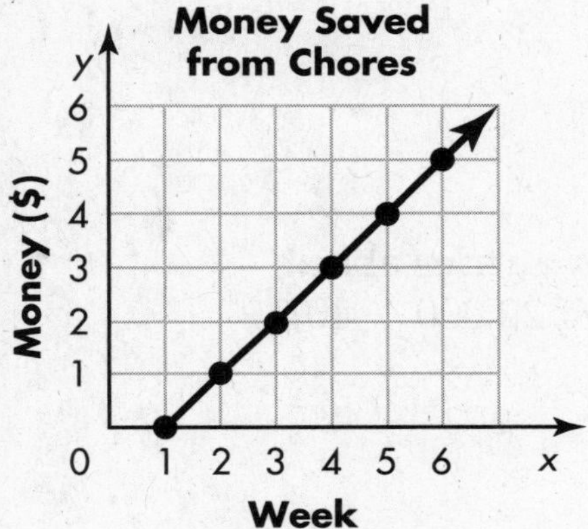

Which equation did Lavon graph?

Ⓕ $y = x + 1$

Ⓖ $y = x - 1$

Ⓗ $y = x + 2$

Ⓘ $y = x - 2$

Go On

3 Ada buys one dozen of each type of muffin. She pays for them with $20.00. How much change does she receive?

Muffin Prices	
Type	**Price per dozen**
Cranberry	$3.00
Blueberry	$4.20
Apple	$4.08
Banana nut	$4.32

Ⓐ $15.60

Ⓑ $5.40

Ⓒ $4.40

Ⓓ $3.40

4 The Sunshine Skyway Bridge across Tampa Bay carries about 20,000 vehicles each day. What is the quotient of 20,000 ÷ 40?

Ⓕ 5,000

Ⓖ 500

Ⓗ 50

Ⓘ 5

Go On

5 How many more inches of precipitation does Jacksonville average than Washington, D.C.?

Average Annual Precipitation of Five U.S. Cities	
City	**Average Annual Precipitation (inches)**
Washington, D.C.	39.35
Savannah, Georgia	49.58
Jacksonville, Florida	52.34
Miami, Florida	58.53
Mobile, Alabama	66.29

Ⓐ 7.01 inches

Ⓑ 11.99 inches

Ⓒ 12.99 inches

Ⓓ 19.18 inches

6 Mr. Johnson gave the list of numbers below to his class. He asked the class to find all the prime numbers in the list.

2, 7, 9, 11

Which of these shows only the prime numbers in Mr. Johnson's list?

Ⓕ 2, 7, 9

Ⓖ 7, 9, 11

Ⓗ 2, 7, 11

Ⓘ 2, 9, 11

Go On

Name ______________________

7 THINK SOLVE EXPLAIN Jonathan wants to buy tickets to a basketball game. Each ticket costs $23.50. Jonathan has $100. Explain how to find the greatest number of tickets Jonathan can buy with $100.

____

____

____

____

____

____

____

____

____

8 The grid below shows some of the exhibits at a zoo.

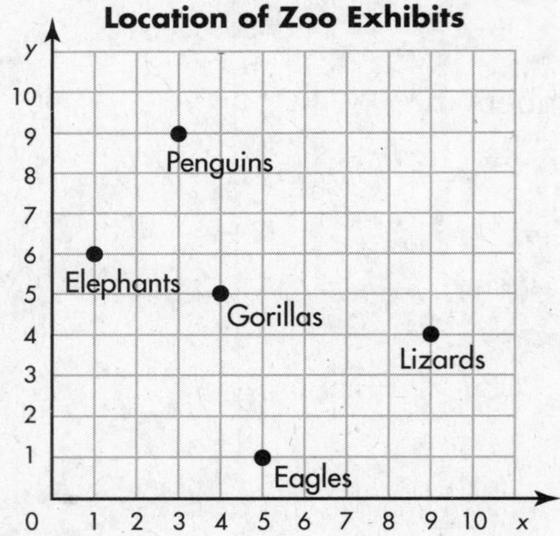

Which exhibit is located at the ordered pair (4, 5)?

Ⓐ Elephants

Ⓑ Eagles

Ⓒ Penguins

Ⓓ Gorillas

Go On

9 Dalia took 163 pictures on her family vacation. She used rolls of film like the one shown below. Which is the best estimate for the number of rolls of film she used to take the pictures?

Ⓕ 8

Ⓖ 6

Ⓗ 4

Ⓘ 2

10 Which statement correctly describes the pattern of the numbers in the grid below?

0.17			
0.27			
0.37	0.38	0.39	0.4
0.47			

Ⓐ Add 1 hundredth for each vertical square and add 1 tenth for each horizontal square.

Ⓑ Add 1 tenth for each vertical square and add 1 hundredth for each horizontal square.

Ⓒ Add 1 tenth for each vertical and horizontal square.

Ⓓ Add 1 hundredth for each vertical square and add 1 thousandth for each horizontal square.

Go On

11 What is the greatest common factor of 36 and 48?

Ⓕ 72

Ⓖ 36

Ⓗ 12

Ⓘ 6

12 The manager of the school's cross-country team recorded the total miles each team member ran after a certain number of weeks. Each team member ran his or her miles equally throughout the weeks they ran.

Student	Number of Weeks	Number of Miles
Joanna	5	105
Antoine	6	108
Veronica	7	133
Andy	4	80

How many miles did Veronica run each week?

Ⓐ 19 miles

Ⓑ 126 miles

Ⓒ 133 miles

Ⓓ 525 miles

Go On

13 Mr. Rahm has a box of tulip bulbs. He wants to plant the bulbs in 20 rows with the same number of bulbs in each row. What is the greatest number of bulbs he can plant in each row, and how many bulbs will be left over?

Ⓕ 9 bulbs in each row with 12 left over

Ⓖ 11 bulbs in each row with 9 left over

Ⓗ 12 bulbs in each row with 0 left over

Ⓘ 12 bulbs in each row with 9 left over

14 Mrs. Guthrie bought all the art supplies below for a class project.

Art Supply Store	
Item	**Price**
Bottle of Paint	$25.95
Paint Brush	$6.60
Pack of Paper	$10.65
Jar of Paste	$4.75

How much did she spend for the bottle of paint and jar of paste?

Ⓐ $30.70

Ⓑ $31.00

Ⓒ $47.95

Ⓓ $73.45

15 Mia is sewing together two lengths of ribbon for an art project. The first piece of ribbon is $\frac{7}{8}$ foot long. The second piece of ribbon is $\frac{1}{12}$ foot long. About how long will the strip of ribbon be?

Ⓕ About $\frac{1}{2}$ foot

Ⓖ About 1 foot

Ⓗ About $1\frac{1}{2}$ feet

Ⓘ About 2 feet

16 Seeds that were taken to the moon in 1971 were then planted in Oregon and Florida. In 2008, the Oregon tree measured 18 feet taller than the Florida tree.

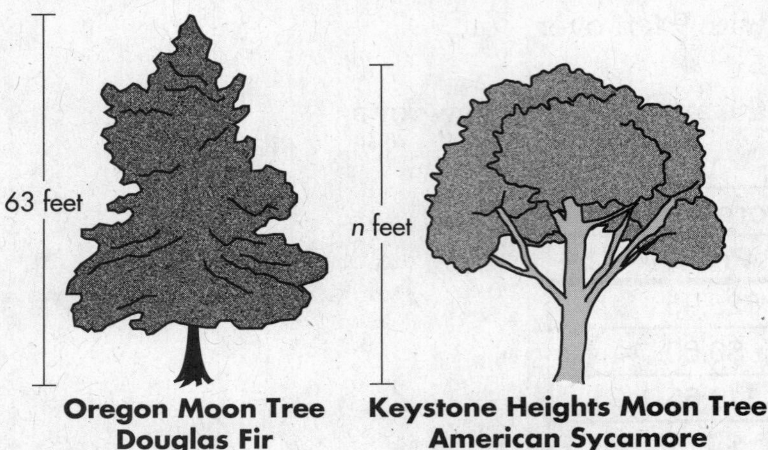

Which equation below can be used to find how tall the Florida tree is?

Ⓐ $n - 18 = 63$

Ⓑ $n + 63 = 18$

Ⓒ $n + 18 = 63$

Ⓓ $18 - n = 63$

Go On

Name ______________________

17 Which fraction shows $\frac{32}{48}$ in simplest form?

Ⓕ $\frac{4}{6}$

Ⓖ $\frac{11}{16}$

Ⓗ $\frac{16}{19}$

Ⓘ $\frac{2}{3}$

18 Lia and her friends have $\frac{7}{8}$ gallon of paint. They painted one outside wall and a door of their clubhouse. The labels below show how much paint they used.

How much paint do they have left after painting one outside wall and the door?

Ⓐ $\frac{3}{4}$ gallon

Ⓑ $\frac{1}{8}$ gallon

Ⓒ $\frac{1}{4}$ gallon

Ⓓ $\frac{3}{8}$ gallon

Go On

Name ______________________________

19 Sergio placed 8 apples in each basket that he packed for the Farmer's Market. He had 145 apples. How many baskets did Sergio fill?

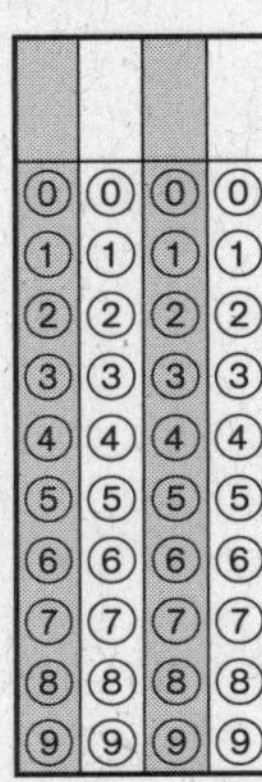

20 A glass patio door is made of two panes of safety glass. There is also a $\frac{1}{4}$ inch space of air between the two panes.

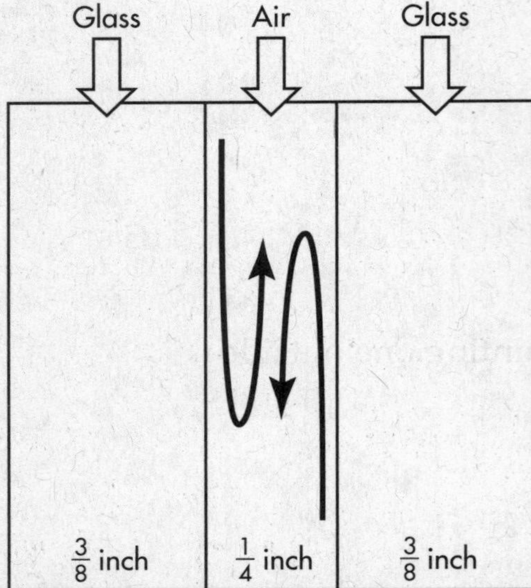

How thick is the entire patio door?

Ⓕ $\frac{1}{2}$ inch

Ⓖ 1 inch

Ⓗ $1\frac{1}{8}$ inches

Ⓘ 2 inches

Go On

21 THINK SOLVE EXPLAIN Mike has 150 files saved on his hard drive. He wants to divide them equally into 5 folders. Explain how a related multiplication fact can help find the number of files that will be in each folder.

____

____

____

____

____

____

____

22 During the annual Coastal Cleanup Day, volunteers help to clean up beaches around the world. The graph shows the number of plastic bottles picked up by 3 student volunteers.

Student Volunteer	Plastic Bottles Picked Up
Yolanda	324
Joshua	253
Kim	212

Yolanda placed an equal number of her bottles into 3 trash bags. How many bottles did she place in each bag?

Ⓐ 18

Ⓑ 32

Ⓒ 103

Ⓓ 108

Go On

Name ___________________________________

23 The University of Florida's Ben Hill Griffin football stadium has a seating capacity of 88,548. If the stadium were divided into 32 equal sections, about how many people would be seated in each section? Use estimation.

Ⓕ About 300

Ⓖ About 400

Ⓗ About 3,000

Ⓘ About 4,000

24 To start practice, the soccer team goes for a jog. They jog from the school to the library and then to the park.

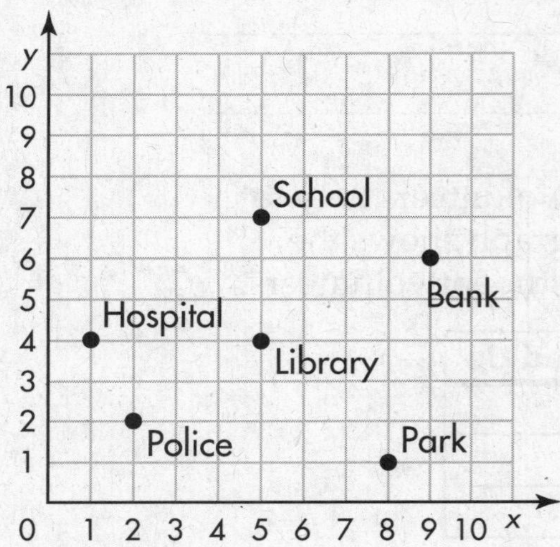

On the map above, each unit represents one block. If they took the shortest route, traveling only horizontally and vertically, how many blocks did they jog?

Ⓐ 5 blocks

Ⓑ 7 blocks

Ⓒ 9 blocks

Ⓓ 11 blocks

Go On

25 Which equation is represented on the number line below?

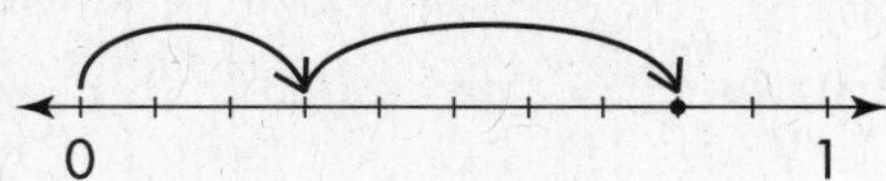

Ⓕ $\frac{3}{10} + \frac{5}{10} = \frac{8}{10}$

Ⓖ $\frac{3}{10} + \frac{8}{10} = \frac{11}{10}$

Ⓗ $\frac{3}{10} + \frac{7}{10} = \frac{10}{10}$

Ⓘ $0 + \frac{3}{10} = \frac{3}{10}$

26 The gift shop at the science museum received a carton of 945 wood dinosaur bones to make models of an exhibit. Museum workers built 27 **identical** dinosaur models from the bones. How many bones does each model contain?

Ⓐ 135

Ⓑ 55

Ⓒ 45

Ⓓ 35

27 A seven-year-old's heart beats 70 times each minute. Which equation below can be used to find how many times the seven-year-old's heart beats in 15 minutes?

Ⓕ $y = 70 + 15$

Ⓖ $y = 70 \times 15$

Ⓗ $70y = 15$

Ⓘ $y - 15 = 70$

28 Mrs. Clausen's class recycled the amounts of paper and glass shown below.

What is the estimate of the total weight of the collected recycled materials?

Ⓐ 12 pounds

Ⓑ 16 pounds

Ⓒ 24 pounds

Ⓓ 29 pounds

Go On

29 Carl and his family went on a trip. The trip odometer shows the distance they have traveled to the nearest tenth of a mile. When they stopped for lunch, the odometer showed the distance below.

What is this distance rounded to the nearest whole mile?

Ⓕ 77

Ⓖ 76.7

Ⓗ 75.7

Ⓘ 76

30 The show *Hello, Dolly!* played at the St. James Theatre in New York City. There were 2,844 performances in 6 years. If each year had the same number of performances, how many performances per year was this?

0	0	0	0
1	1	1	1
2	2	2	2
3	3	3	3
4	4	4	4
5	5	5	5
6	6	6	6
7	7	7	7
8	8	8	8
9	9	9	9

Go On

31 In an election for class president, $\frac{27}{50}$ of the student population voted for Candidate A, $\frac{11}{50}$ of the student population voted for Candidate B, and the rest of the student population did not vote. What fraction of the student population voted more for Candidate A than for Candidate B?

Ⓐ $\frac{6}{25}$

Ⓑ $\frac{8}{25}$

Ⓒ $\frac{31}{50}$

Ⓓ $\frac{19}{25}$

32 Complete the factor tree below to find the prime factorization of 32.

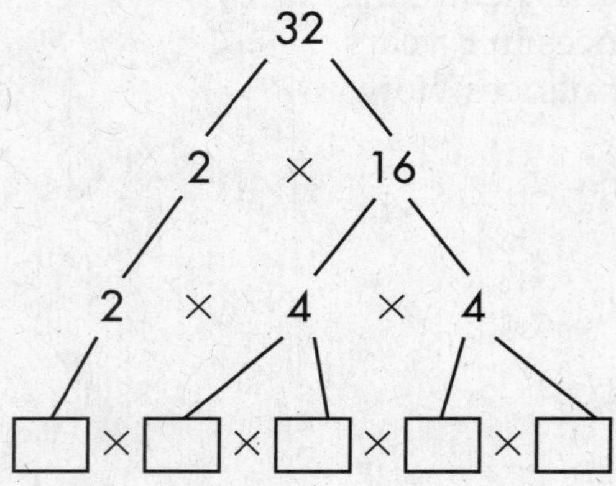

Ⓕ 2^5

Ⓖ 1×2^4

Ⓗ 2×4^4

Ⓘ $1^2 \times 2^2 \times 4^2$

Go On

33 What is the horizontal distance between Point P and Point M?

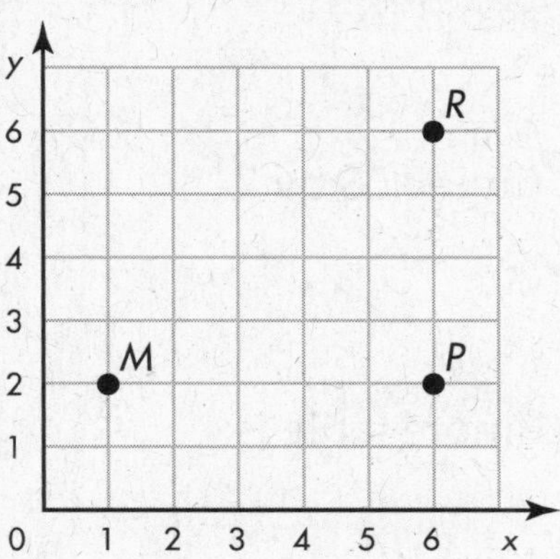

Ⓐ 4

Ⓑ 5

Ⓒ 6

Ⓓ 7

34 Paula raises rabbits as a hobby. She made the table below to help her know how much to feed the rabbits.

Weight of Rabbit	Amount of Food
8–10 pounds	$\frac{3}{8}$ cup
11–15 pounds	$\frac{2}{3}$ cup

How much more food does Paula feed her 13-pound rabbit than her 9-pound rabbit?

Ⓕ $\frac{1}{5}$ cup

Ⓖ $\frac{1}{3}$ cup

Ⓗ $\frac{5}{11}$ cup

Ⓘ $\frac{7}{24}$ cup

35 There are 58 people at a picnic and 8 people can be seated at each table. Which answer is reasonable if you are asked to find the number of tables needed to seat everyone?

Ⓐ 2 tables because there are 2 leftover when you divide 58 by 7

Ⓑ 6 tables because I estimated using rounding

Ⓒ 7 tables because $58 \div 8 = 7$ with 2 leftover

Ⓓ 8 tables because $58 \div 8 = 7$ with 2 leftover, so 1 more table is needed for the remaining 2 people

36 Jane noticed that the temperature was 9°F when she got home from school. For the next four hours, the temperature dropped 2°F each hour. Jane made the table of values below for $y = 9 - 2x$.

$y = 9 - 2x$	
x	y
1	7
2	5
3	
4	1

Which number is missing in Jane's table of values for $y = 9 - 2x$?

Ⓕ 12

Ⓖ 5

Ⓗ 3

Ⓘ 2

Go On

Name ___________________________________

37 Josh needs to add to find what fraction of the days in March were cloudy, sunny, and rainy.

March Weather Data

Conditions	Fraction Part of March
Rainy	$\frac{1}{2}$
Sunny	$\frac{1}{6}$
Cloudy	$\frac{4}{15}$
Snowy	$\frac{1}{15}$

What is the least common denominator Josh should use to find the sum?

0	0	0	0
1	1	1	1
2	2	2	2
3	3	3	3
4	4	4	4
5	5	5	5
6	6	6	6
7	7	7	7
8	8	8	8
9	9	9	9

38 Jason sent out invitations to 3 friends for his party. Each friend invited 3 other friends to the party. Then, each of those friends invited 3 more friends. The total number of people invited to Jason's party can be represented by $3 \times 3 \times 3$. Written in exponential notation, how many people were invited to the party?

Ⓐ 3^1

Ⓑ 3^2

Ⓒ 3^3

Ⓓ 3^4

STOP

Name ____________________

1. Alyssa spent $1.86 on a package of scrapbook paper and $0.79 on a glue stick. What is the total amount she spent?

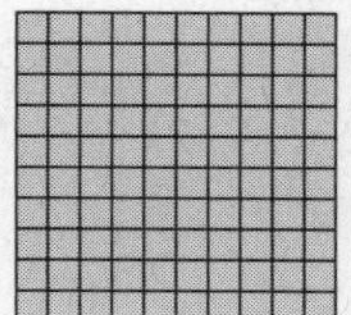 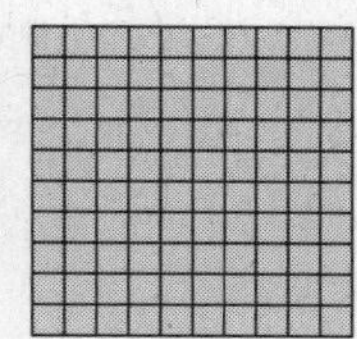 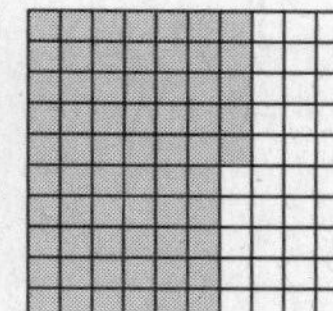

Ⓐ $2.65 Ⓒ $1.65
Ⓑ $2.55 Ⓓ $1.55

2. Use the model to find the sum of 0.78 + 1.46.

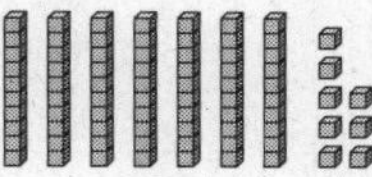 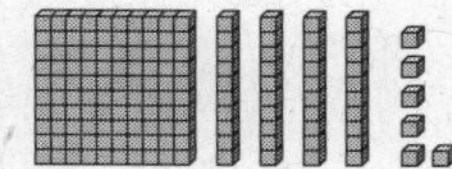

Ⓕ 1.24
Ⓖ 1.53
Ⓗ 2.24
Ⓘ 3.24

3. Explain how you can use place-value blocks to find the difference of 2.56 − 1.65.

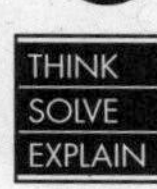

____
____
____
____
____
____
____
____
____

Go On

4 Use the model below. What is the sum of $\frac{3}{8}$ and $\frac{2}{8}$?

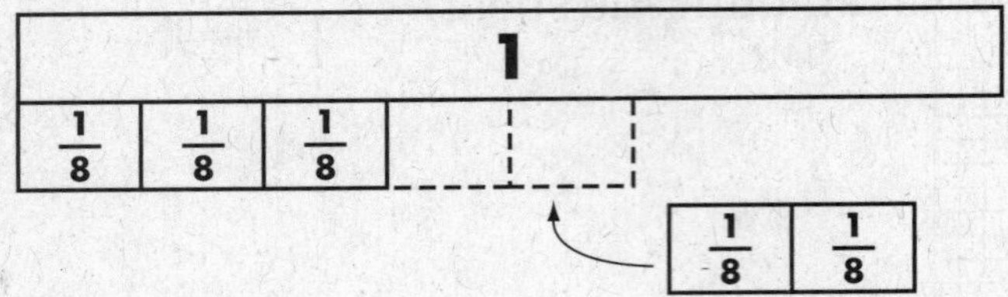

Ⓐ $\frac{2}{8}$

Ⓑ $\frac{3}{8}$

Ⓒ $\frac{5}{8}$

Ⓓ $\frac{7}{8}$

5 A recipe calls for $\frac{3}{4}$ cup of shredded carrots. Callie has already shredded $\frac{1}{4}$ cup of carrots. How much more carrot should she shred?

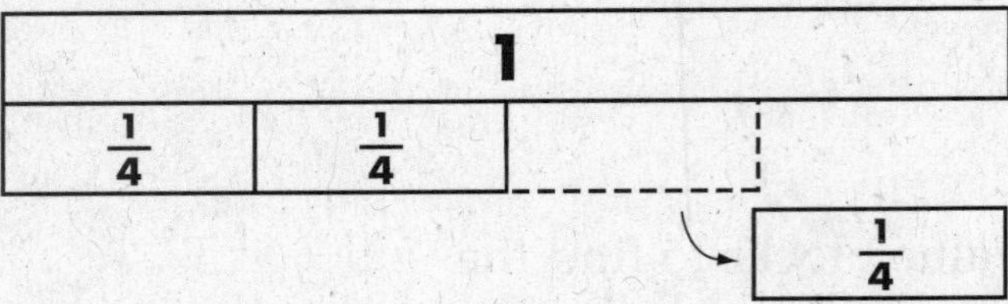

Ⓕ $\frac{1}{4}$ cup

Ⓖ $\frac{2}{4}$ cup

Ⓗ $\frac{3}{4}$ cup

Ⓘ $\frac{4}{4}$ cup

6 The number line shows which of the following equations?

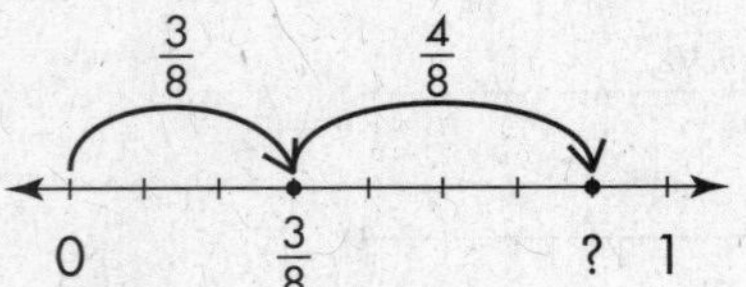

Start

Ⓐ $\frac{4}{4} - \frac{3}{4} = \frac{1}{4}$

Ⓑ $\frac{3}{8} + \frac{4}{8} = \frac{7}{8}$

Ⓒ $\frac{1}{8} + \frac{4}{8} = \frac{5}{8}$

Ⓓ $\frac{7}{8} - \frac{4}{8} = \frac{3}{8}$

Go On

7 What is the least common denominator for $\frac{1}{6}$ and $\frac{3}{8}$?

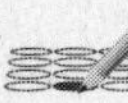

0	0	0	0
1	1	1	1
2	2	2	2
3	3	3	3
4	4	4	4
5	5	5	5
6	6	6	6
7	7	7	7
8	8	8	8
9	9	9	9

8 What is the sum of $\frac{7}{12} + \frac{1}{4}$ in simplest form?

Ⓕ $\frac{11}{12}$

Ⓖ $\frac{5}{6}$

Ⓗ $\frac{1}{3}$

Ⓘ $\frac{8}{12}$

9 Darius has $\frac{1}{3}$ quart of juice. Rita has $\frac{1}{4}$ quart of juice. How much more juice does Darius have than Rita?

Ⓐ $\frac{1}{3}$ quart

Ⓑ $\frac{1}{4}$ quart

Ⓒ $\frac{1}{8}$ quart

Ⓓ $\frac{1}{12}$ quart

10 The school store has the following items for sale. Jenna bought one of each item. If Jenna paid for the items with a $10 bill, how much change did she receive?

Ⓕ $8.80

Ⓖ $7.80

Ⓗ $6.80

Ⓘ $2.20

11 What is the sum of $\frac{1}{11} + \frac{3}{11} + \frac{4}{11}$?

Ⓐ $\frac{7}{11}$ Ⓒ $\frac{7}{22}$

Ⓑ $\frac{8}{11}$ Ⓓ $\frac{8}{33}$

12 Monday night Tyrell spent $\frac{2}{6}$ hour on his homework and Eva spent $\frac{5}{6}$ hour her homework. How much more time did Eva spend on homework than Tyrell?

Ⓕ $\frac{1}{2}$ hour Ⓗ $\frac{1}{6}$ hour

Ⓖ $\frac{1}{3}$ hour Ⓘ $1\frac{1}{6}$ hours

13 Gia walked $\frac{1}{4}$ mile from her house to the park, then $\frac{3}{8}$ mile around the park, and then $\frac{1}{4}$ mile back home. How many miles did she walk in all?

Ⓐ $\frac{4}{8}$ mile

Ⓑ $\frac{4}{12}$ mile

Ⓒ $\frac{7}{8}$ mile

Ⓓ $\frac{8}{8}$ mile

14 The adult leaf-footed bug found in Florida is about $\frac{3}{4}$ inch long. The adult thorn bug is about $\frac{1}{2}$ inch long. How much longer is the leaf-footed bug than the thorn bug?

$\frac{3}{4}$ in. long

$\frac{1}{2}$	x

Ⓕ $\frac{2}{4}$ inch

Ⓖ $\frac{3}{8}$ inch

Ⓗ $\frac{1}{4}$ inch

Ⓘ $\frac{1}{6}$ inch

Go On

15 The height of Mount McKinley in Alaska is about 3.848 miles. What is the height of Mount McKinley, rounded to the nearest tenth?

Ⓐ 3.0
Ⓑ 3.8
Ⓒ 3.9
Ⓓ 4.0

16 The table below shows the number of peanuts found in different snacks.

Food Item	Number of Peanuts
Box of Trail Mix	98.7
Energy Bar	35.4
Cookie	3.8

What is the most reasonable estimate for the total number of peanuts in the snacks?

Ⓕ 120
Ⓖ 123
Ⓗ 144
Ⓘ 158

17 Which is the best estimate of $\frac{2}{5} + \frac{1}{7}$?

Ⓐ $\frac{1}{2} + 0 = \frac{1}{2}$
Ⓑ $0 + 1 = 1$
Ⓒ $\frac{1}{2} + \frac{1}{2} = 1$
Ⓓ $1 + 1 = 2$

18 Ted needs enough pretzels for each of the 9 players on his baseball team to have an equal number. Which of the following numbers is divisible by 9?

Ⓕ 261
Ⓖ 239
Ⓗ 181
Ⓘ 118

Go On

19 Which of the following is a prime number?

Ⓐ 21

Ⓑ 69

Ⓒ 73

Ⓓ 80

20 There are 100 senators in the United States Senate. What is the prime factorization of 100?

Ⓕ 2×5^2

Ⓖ $2^2 \times 5^2$

Ⓗ 10×10

Ⓘ $2^2 \times 5$

21 The ordered pair (2, 5) is included on which of the following graphs?

Ⓐ $y = 2x - 1$

Ⓑ $y = 2x + 1$

Ⓒ $y = 2x$

Ⓓ $y = 1 - 2x$

22 What is the ordered pair for Point *S*?

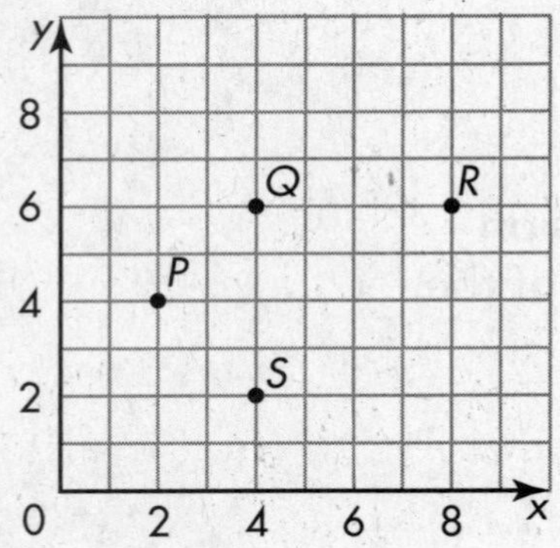

Ⓕ (2, 4)

Ⓖ (6, 4)

Ⓗ (4, 6)

Ⓘ (4, 2)

Go On

23 Which shows how to find the horizontal distance between (3, 4) and (8, 4)?

Ⓐ Subtract y-values: $4 - 4 = 0$ units.
Ⓑ Add y-values $4 + 4 = 8$ units.
Ⓒ Subtract x-values: $8 - 3 = 5$ units.
Ⓓ Add x-values: $8 + 3 = 11$ units.

24 

Jamie and a friend start a dog-washing business. The graph shows how many dogs they wash in one week. Write a short story of what happens during the week with the business.

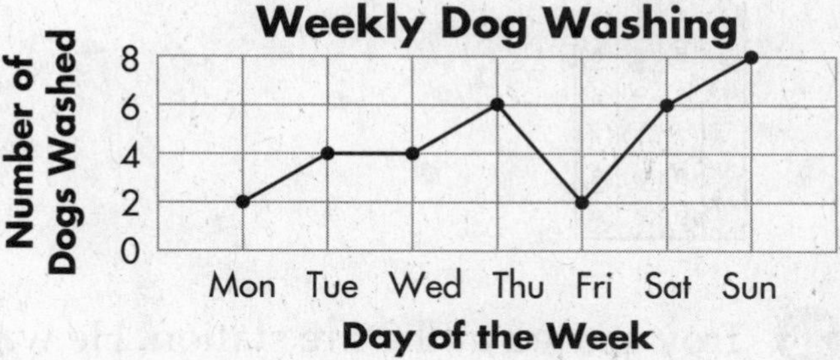

____

____

____

____

____

____

____

____

25 The Withlacoochee State Forest in Florida has 44 miles of bike trails and 64 miles of canoe trails. What is the greatest common factor of 44 and 64?

Ⓕ 11
Ⓖ 8
Ⓗ 6
Ⓘ 4

26 Which fraction is NOT in simplest form?

Ⓐ $\frac{7}{21}$
Ⓑ $\frac{3}{8}$
Ⓒ $\frac{5}{54}$
Ⓓ $\frac{1}{8}$

Go On

Name ________________________________

27 What is the least common multiple of 8 and 12?

0	0	0	0
1	1	1	1
2	2	2	2
3	3	3	3
4	4	4	4
5	5	5	5
6	6	6	6
7	7	7	7
8	8	8	8
9	9	9	9

28 Troy started at the fire station. He walked to the library and then rode his bike to the post office. If Troy took the shortest route, how far did he travel?

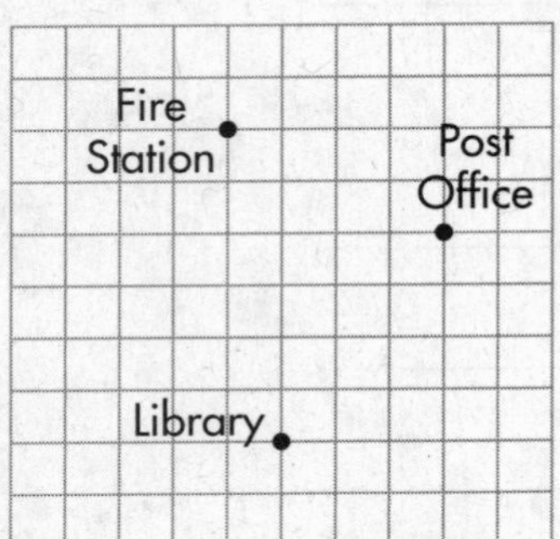

Ⓕ 6 blocks Ⓗ 14 blocks

Ⓖ 13 blocks Ⓘ 21 blocks

29 Look for a pattern. Which of the following can be placed in the empty box to complete the grid?

0.12	0.13	0.14
	0.23	

Ⓐ 0.35 Ⓒ 0.24

Ⓑ 0.25 Ⓓ 0.15

30 Which supports the conjecture that the product of two odd numbers is an odd number?

Ⓕ $4 \times 1 = 4$ Ⓗ $2 \times 5 = 10$

Ⓖ $7 \times 12 = 84$ Ⓘ $9 \times 3 = 27$

STOP

Name ______________________________

1 Which improper fraction does the model show? (9-1)

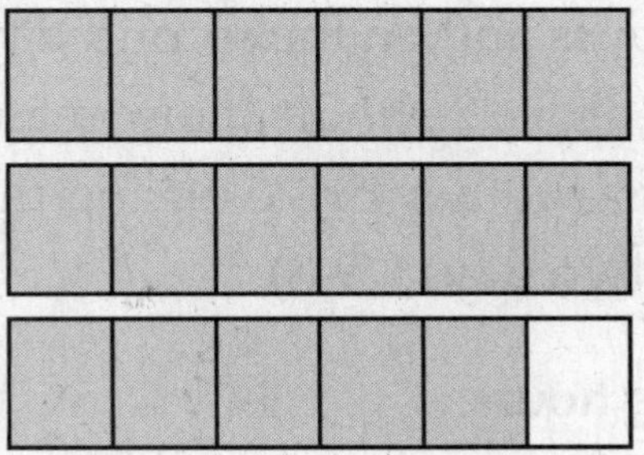

Ⓐ $\frac{17}{6}$

Ⓑ $\frac{11}{6}$

Ⓒ $\frac{7}{6}$

Ⓓ $\frac{6}{6}$

2 Cal made $\frac{18}{4}$ gallons of orange juice for a big party. What is $\frac{18}{4}$ expressed as a mixed number? (9-1)

Ⓕ $5\frac{1}{2}$

Ⓖ $5\frac{1}{8}$

Ⓗ $4\frac{1}{2}$

Ⓘ $4\frac{1}{4}$

3 Which expression does the model show? (9-2)

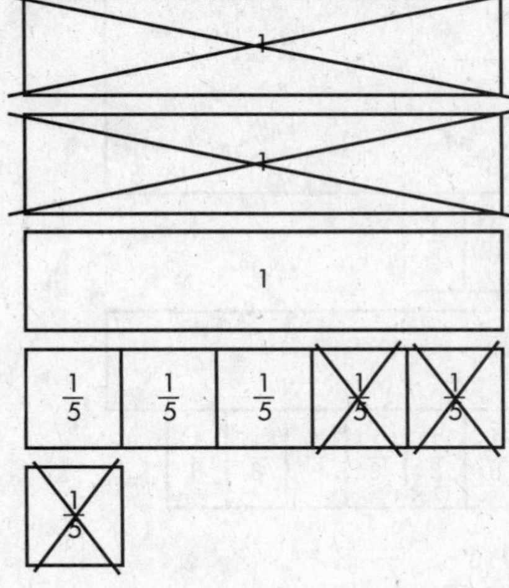

Ⓐ $3\frac{6}{5} - 2$

Ⓑ $4\frac{1}{5} - 2\frac{3}{5}$

Ⓒ $3\frac{5}{5} - 2\frac{1}{5}$

Ⓓ $4\frac{1}{5} - 2\frac{1}{5}$

4 Ricky needs $3\frac{1}{4}$ cups of sugar to make muffins. He already has $2\frac{1}{2}$ cups. How many more cups of sugar does he need? (9-4)

Ⓕ $2\frac{1}{3}$ cups

Ⓖ $1\frac{1}{4}$ cups

Ⓗ $\frac{3}{4}$ cup

Ⓘ $\frac{1}{2}$ cup

5 Judy bought $8\frac{3}{4}$ pounds of oranges. Which improper fraction equals $8\frac{3}{4}$? (9-1)

Ⓐ $\frac{15}{4}$

Ⓑ $\frac{27}{4}$

Ⓒ $\frac{32}{4}$

Ⓓ $\frac{35}{4}$

Go On

6 Which expression does the model show? (9-2)

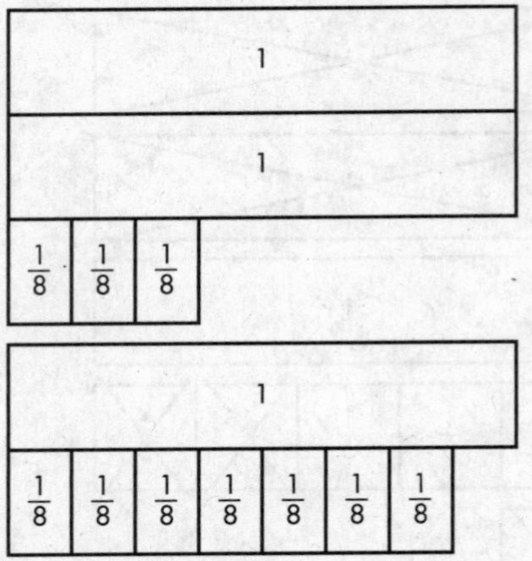

Ⓕ $2\frac{3}{8} + 1\frac{7}{8}$

Ⓖ $\frac{5}{8} + \frac{8}{8}$

Ⓗ $\frac{11}{8} + \frac{15}{8}$

Ⓘ $\frac{8}{8} + \frac{8}{8}$

7 Casey and Bret are doing their book reports. Casey has written $2\frac{5}{8}$ pages. Bret has written $\frac{3}{4}$ of a page less than Casey. How many pages has Bret written? (9-4)

Ⓐ $2\frac{3}{8}$

Ⓑ $2\frac{1}{4}$

Ⓒ $1\frac{7}{8}$

Ⓓ $1\frac{1}{8}$

8 The Petersons went on a 300-mile trip. On the first day, they drove $3\frac{5}{6}$ hours and on the second day they drove $2\frac{1}{3}$ hours. How many hours did they drive during the first two days? (9-3)

Ⓕ $8\frac{1}{3}$ hours

Ⓖ $6\frac{1}{6}$ hours

Ⓗ 5 hours

Ⓘ $3\frac{7}{8}$ hours

9 Which equation matches the picture? (9-6)

x	
$1\frac{1}{3}$	$4\frac{5}{12}$

Ⓐ $4\frac{5}{12} - 1\frac{1}{3} = x$

Ⓑ $1\frac{1}{3} + 4\frac{5}{12} = x$

Ⓒ $x + 1\frac{1}{3} = 4\frac{5}{12}$

Ⓓ $x + 4\frac{5}{12} = 1\frac{1}{3}$

10 What is the sum of $2\frac{3}{5} + 3\frac{1}{4}$? (9-3)

Ⓕ $6\frac{3}{20}$

Ⓖ $6\frac{1}{20}$

Ⓗ $5\frac{19}{20}$

Ⓘ $5\frac{17}{20}$

Go On

Name ______________________________

11 What is the sum of $4\frac{5}{6} + 3\frac{2}{6}$? (9-2)

1
1
1
1

$\frac{1}{6}$	$\frac{1}{6}$	$\frac{1}{6}$	$\frac{1}{6}$	$\frac{1}{6}$

1
1
1

$\frac{1}{6}$	$\frac{1}{6}$

Ⓐ $6\frac{1}{2}$ Ⓒ $7\frac{1}{6}$

Ⓑ $6\frac{5}{6}$ Ⓓ $8\frac{1}{6}$

12 Cynthia says that when you evaluate the expression $(21\frac{3}{4} + 4\frac{1}{2}) - 5\frac{3}{12}$ you get a whole number. What whole number do you get? (9-5)

0	0	0	0
1	1	1	1
2	2	2	2
3	3	3	3
4	4	4	4
5	5	5	5
6	6	6	6
7	7	7	7
8	8	8	8
9	9	9	9

13 THINK SOLVE EXPLAIN

Jason measured rainfall for a science project. Last week it rained $3\frac{1}{8}$ inches in all. This week it rained $1\frac{7}{8}$ inches on one day and $2\frac{3}{4}$ inches on another. How many more inches did it rain this week than last week? Explain how you found your answer.

____

____

____

____

____

____

____

____

____

____

____

____

STOP

Topic 9 Florida Test

Name ___________________________

Mark the best answer.

1 Use an inch ruler. To the nearest $\frac{1}{2}$ inch, how long is the segment? (10-1)

Ⓐ 1 in.

Ⓑ $1\frac{1}{2}$ in.

Ⓒ 2 in.

Ⓓ $2\frac{1}{2}$ in.

2 Which of the following is true? (10-4)

Ⓕ 3.5 m < 35 cm

Ⓖ 5 cm = 50 mm

Ⓗ 1,000 mm > 9 m

Ⓘ 8 m < 750 cm

3 Which is the most precise measure? (10-1)

Ⓐ To the nearest inch

Ⓑ To the nearest $\frac{1}{2}$ inch

Ⓒ To the nearest $\frac{1}{4}$ inch

Ⓓ To the nearest $\frac{1}{8}$ inch

4 Which is the best unit of measure for measuring the length of a highway? (10-3)

Ⓕ meter

Ⓖ millimeter

Ⓗ centimeter

Ⓘ kilometer

5 The Airbus A380 airplane is 79 feet 1 inch tall. How many inches tall is the airplane? (10-2)

Ⓐ 80 inches

Ⓑ 929 inches

Ⓒ 939 inches

Ⓓ 949 inches

6 Juan measured his desk and found it to be 90 centimeters wide. How many millimeters is the width of his desk? (10-4)

Ⓕ 9,000 millimeters

Ⓖ 900 millimeters

Ⓗ 90 millimeters

Ⓘ 9 millimeters

Go On

Name ____________________

7 Use the inch ruler shown. To the nearest $\frac{1}{4}$ inch, how long is the key? (10-1)

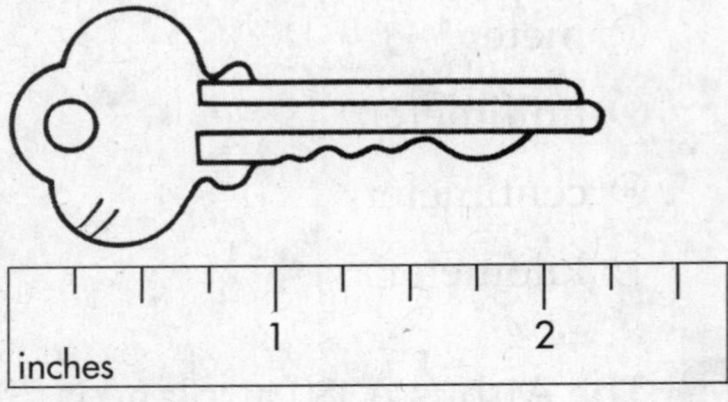

Ⓐ $2\frac{1}{2}$ inches

Ⓑ $2\frac{3}{8}$ inches

Ⓒ $2\frac{1}{4}$ inches

Ⓓ $2\frac{3}{4}$ inches

8 A fully grown blue whale can be 30 meters in length. How would you find how many centimeters are equal to 30 meters? (10-4)

Ⓕ 30×10

Ⓖ 30×100

Ⓗ $30 \times 1{,}000$

Ⓘ $30 \times 10{,}000$

9 Use a centimeter ruler. Which line segment measures closest to 57 millimeters long? (10-3)

Ⓐ ├──────────┤

Ⓑ ├───────┤

Ⓒ ├────────────┤

Ⓓ ├─────────────┤

10 Which inequality is NOT true? (10-2)

Ⓕ 200 in. $>$ 15 ft

Ⓖ 3 yd $<$ 112 in.

Ⓗ 12 ft. 1 in. $>$ 3 yd 7 in.

Ⓘ 2 ft 24 in. $>$ 1 yd 1 ft

11 Newtown High School is building a new football field. The field must be at least 360 feet long. The land behind the school is 4,344 inches long. Is the land long enough to make a football field? (10-2)

Ⓐ Yes, because 4,344 inches = 362 feet and $362 > 360$.

Ⓑ Yes, because 4,344 inches = 360 feet and $360 = 360$.

Ⓒ No, because 4,344 inches = 350 feet and $350 < 360$.

Ⓓ No, because 4,344 inches = 355 feet and $355 < 360$.

Name ____________________

12 The Choo family is putting new tiles in their entryway. Each tile is a 1-foot square. If the area of the entryway is 28 square feet, which of the following could be the perimeter of the entryway? (10-5)

Ⓕ 20 feet

Ⓖ 22 feet

Ⓗ 26 feet

Ⓘ 28 feet

13 Which is equivalent to the distance that Tom ran? (10-4)

Student	Distance Run
Tom	5 km 500 m
Ron	3,200 m
Ben	1,800 m
Molly	2 km 700 m

Ⓐ 5,000 meters

Ⓑ 5,500 meters

Ⓒ 6,000 meters

Ⓓ 6,600 meters

14 The length of an ear of corn is 190 millimeters. How many centimeters is this? (10-4)

0	0	0	0
1	1	1	1
2	2	2	2
3	3	3	3
4	4	4	4
5	5	5	5
6	6	6	6
7	7	7	7
8	8	8	8
9	9	9	9

15 THINK SOLVE EXPLAIN

Marta has twenty 1-foot × 1-foot square patio blocks to arrange in the shape of a rectangle in her back yard. She wants the perimeter of the rectangle to be greater than 20 feet. Use grid paper and make an organized list to find all possible arrangements. Which arrangement(s) can she use? (10-5)

____

____

____

____

____

____

STOP

Name ____________________

Mark the best answer.

1 Which inequality is NOT true? (11-4)

Ⓐ 30 g > 300 mg

Ⓑ 100 mg > 100 kg

Ⓒ 999,999 mg < 1 kg

Ⓓ 5 g < 50 kg

2 Which of these units would you use to measure the weight of one lime? (11-1)

Ⓕ Tons

Ⓖ Ounces

Ⓗ Pounds

Ⓘ Inches

3 Which is the most appropriate unit to measure the mass of a basketball? (11-3)

Ⓐ Grams

Ⓑ Kilograms

Ⓒ Meters

Ⓓ Kilometers

4 A package of pasta says that the suggested serving size is 56 grams before it is cooked. How many milligrams is this? (11-4)

Ⓕ 5.6 milligrams

Ⓖ 56 milligrams

Ⓗ 5,600 milligrams

Ⓘ 56,000 milligrams

5 Which unit would best measure the weight of a large dog? (11-1)

Ⓐ Tons

Ⓑ Ounces

Ⓒ Pounds

Ⓓ Grams

6 Timmy's birthday is 53 days away. Which of these amounts of time is greater than 53 days? (11-5)

Ⓕ 3 weeks

Ⓖ 2,400 hours

Ⓗ 1 month

Ⓘ 240 hours

Go On

7 Donna and her friend Cassie were born on the same date but exactly one year apart. Neither of them was born in a leap year. How many days apart were they born? (11-5)

Ⓐ 100 days
Ⓑ 365 days
Ⓒ 366 days
Ⓓ 1,000 days

8 Angela's solo in the school musical lasted 157 seconds. Which symbol makes the comparison true? (11-5)

157 seconds ◯ 3 minutes

Ⓕ ×
Ⓖ <
Ⓗ =
Ⓘ >

9 Louie noticed that the temperature inside his house rose at an average of 2°F every 15 minutes. Louie's house has a temperature of 69°F at 10:30 A.M. Make a table to find the expected time for his house to reach 81°F. (11-6)

Ⓐ 12:15 A.M.
Ⓑ 11:45 A.M.
Ⓒ 12:00 P.M.
Ⓓ 12:30 P.M.

10 Which of the following can be used to find how many kilograms of chopped fresh tomatoes the recipe calls for? (11-4)

Salsa Recipe
5,000 grams chopped fresh tomatoes
2,500 grams chopped peppers
1,500 grams chopped cilantro
500 grams chopped onions

Ⓕ 5,000 ÷ 1,000
Ⓖ 5,000 ÷ 100
Ⓗ 5,000 × 1,000
Ⓘ 5,000 × 100

11 The Babbit family grows pumpkins on their farm. One year, they grew a pumpkin that weighed 74 pounds. How many ounces did it weigh? (11-2)

Ⓐ 16 oz
Ⓑ 48 oz
Ⓒ 1,184 oz
Ⓓ 2,368 oz

12 A male lion weighs about 400 pounds. How many tons would 15 lions weigh? (11-2)

Ⓕ $\frac{1}{2}$ ton
Ⓖ 3 tons
Ⓗ 4 tons
Ⓘ 5 tons

Go On

Name ______________________________

Mark the best answer.

13 Which is a good estimate for the mass of an average newborn baby? (11-3)

Ⓐ 3,000 kilograms

Ⓑ 300 kilograms

Ⓒ 30 kilograms

Ⓓ 3 kilograms

14 How many weeks are there in three years? (11-5)

0	0	0	0
1	1	1	1
2	2	2	2
3	3	3	3
4	4	4	4
5	5	5	5
6	6	6	6
7	7	7	7
8	8	8	8
9	9	9	9

15 

Robert entered his name into a prize raffle at 6:00 P.M. After he entered his name, a new winner was called every 12 minutes. Robert was the sixth name to be called. At what time was Robert's name called? Make a table to find this time. (11-6)

____

STOP

Name ____________________

1 What is the area of a parallelogram whose base measures 6 centimeters and height measures 8 centimeters? (12-3)

Ⓐ 14 cm^2
Ⓑ 24 cm^2
Ⓒ 36 cm^2
Ⓓ 48 cm^2

2 Which of the following degree measures is closest to the measure of the angle shown? (12-1)

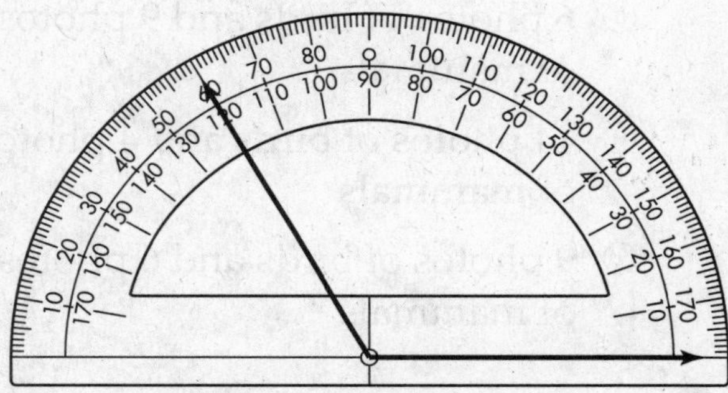

Ⓕ 60°
Ⓖ 70°
Ⓗ 120°
Ⓘ 140°

3 A section of stained glass is in the shape of a trapezoid. If the bases of the trapezoid are 2 centimeters and 6 centimeters and the height is 4 centimeters, what is the area of the trapezoid? (12-5)

Ⓐ 16 cm^2
Ⓑ 10 cm^2
Ⓒ 6 cm^2
Ⓓ 4 cm^2

4 The area of the rectangle below is 42 square yards. Which of the following can be used to find the area of the shaded triangle? (12-4)

Ⓕ $42 \div 2$
Ⓖ 42
Ⓗ $42 - 7$
Ⓘ $42 - (2 \times 7)$

5 What is the area of a rectangular billboard that has a base of 33 feet and a height of 12 feet? (12-2)

Ⓐ 99 ft^2
Ⓑ 360 ft^2
Ⓒ 369 ft^2
Ⓓ 396 ft^2

Go On

Name ______________________________

6 Which is the area of the vegetable garden? (12-4)

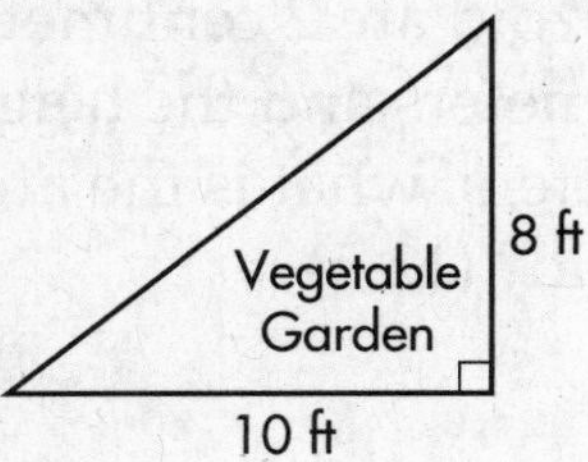

Ⓕ 40 ft

Ⓖ 40 ft^2

Ⓗ 80 ft

Ⓘ 80 ft^2

7 What is the area of the entire floor space? (12-6)

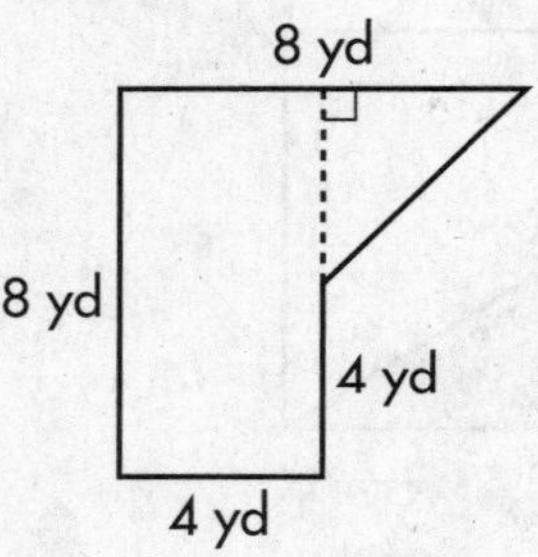

Ⓐ 44 yd^2

Ⓑ 40 yd^2

Ⓒ 36 yd^2

Ⓓ 32 yd^2

8 Anita is making a photo collage of animals with an area of 48 square inches. Each photo of a bird has an area of 2 square inches. Each photo of a mammal has an area of 5 square inches. If Anita wants to use 3 more photos of birds than mammals, how many photos of birds and how many photos of mammals should she use to fill the entire area? (12-7)

Ⓕ 13 photos of birds and 10 photos of mammals

Ⓖ 6 photos of birds and 9 photos of mammals

Ⓗ 14 photos of birds and 4 photos of mammals

Ⓘ 9 photos of birds and 6 photos of mammals

9 Which best classifies the angle shown? (12-1)

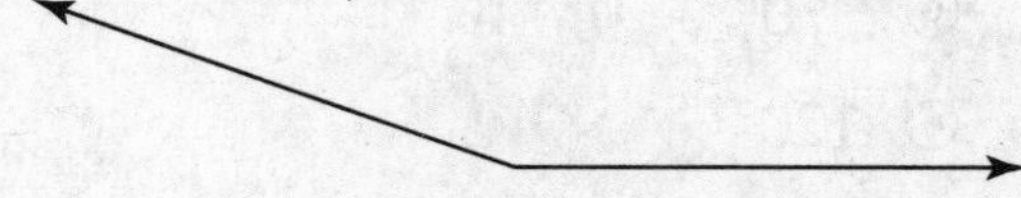

Ⓐ Right

Ⓑ Acute

Ⓒ Obtuse

Ⓓ Straight

Go On

Name ___________________________

10 Ms. Murphy's classroom is in the shape of a square. The measure of one side is 34 feet. Which expression can be used to find the area of her classroom? (12-2)

Ⓕ 2×34

Ⓖ 34×4

Ⓗ $34 + 34 + 34 + 34$

Ⓘ 34×34

11 What is the area of the entire figure? (12-6)

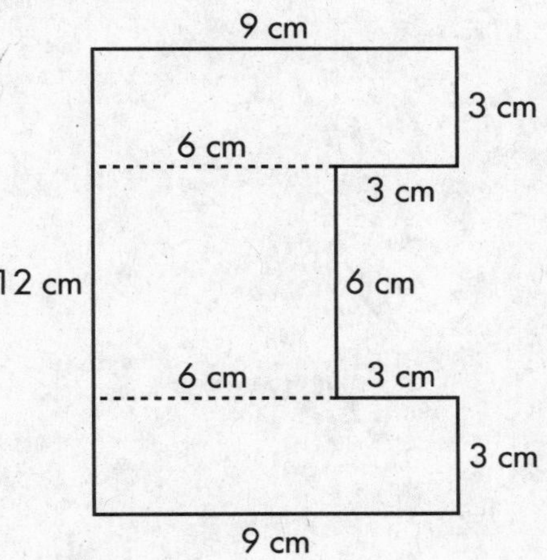

Ⓐ 54 cm^2

Ⓑ 72 cm^2

Ⓒ 90 cm^2

Ⓓ 108 cm^2

12 Denise draws a parallelogram on grid paper. The base is 12 units and the height is 7 units. How many square units is the area? (12-3)

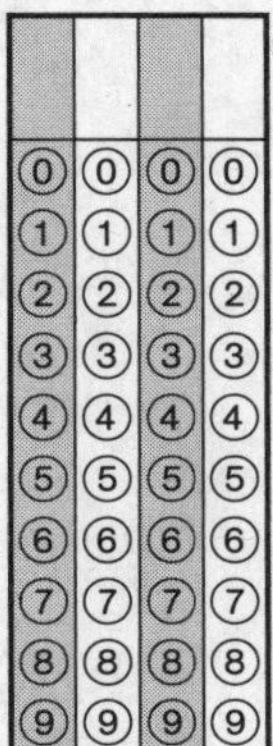

13 THINK SOLVE EXPLAIN

Jaime wants to carpet a room that is 30 feet × 24 feet. He wants the carpet to be in a checkerboard pattern, so he needs to buy squares of carpet. The squares of carpet come as 5 feet × 5 feet, 3 feet × 3 feet, or 2 feet × 2 feet. Which size will Jaime NOT be able to use if he wants to use only whole-carpet squares? Explain. (12-7)

____

____

____

____

____

STOP

Topic 12 Florida Test

Name ______________________________

1 Ken ate $\frac{5}{3}$ containers of yogurt. What is $\frac{5}{3}$ expressed as a mixed number?

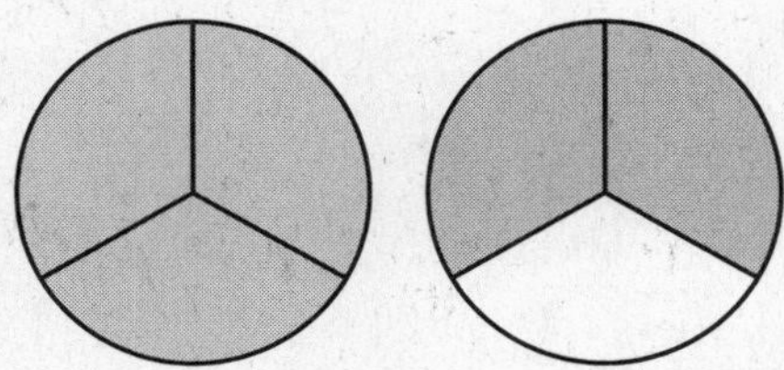

Ⓐ $5\frac{1}{3}$

Ⓑ $2\frac{3}{5}$

Ⓒ $1\frac{2}{3}$

Ⓓ $1\frac{1}{3}$

2 Mike needs $1\frac{4}{8}$ cups of flour to make a cake and $1\frac{7}{8}$ cups of flour to make a piecrust. How much flour does Mike need to bake the cake and piecrust? Use the model to find the sum.

1			
$\frac{1}{8}$	$\frac{1}{8}$	$\frac{1}{8}$	$\frac{1}{8}$

1						
$\frac{1}{8}$	$\frac{1}{8}$	$\frac{1}{8}$	$\frac{1}{8}$	$\frac{1}{8}$	$\frac{1}{8}$	$\frac{1}{8}$

Ⓕ $1\frac{3}{8}$ cups

Ⓖ 2 cups

Ⓗ $2\frac{8}{10}$ cups

Ⓘ $3\frac{3}{8}$ cups

3 Javier hiked in Suwanee State Park on Saturday. First he hiked $1\frac{1}{2}$ miles on the San Hills Trail. Then he hiked $1\frac{7}{10}$ miles on the Suwannee River Trail. How many miles did he hike on Saturday?

Ⓐ $3\frac{1}{5}$ miles

Ⓑ $2\frac{1}{5}$ miles

Ⓒ $2\frac{10}{20}$ miles

Ⓓ 2 miles

Go On

Benchmark Test 3
Topics 9–12

4 What is the difference of $2\frac{3}{8} - 1\frac{1}{4}$?

Ⓕ $\frac{1}{8}$

Ⓖ $\frac{7}{8}$

Ⓗ $1\frac{1}{8}$

Ⓘ $1\frac{1}{2}$

5 Tyree is reading a book that is $2\frac{1}{4}$ inches thick. Olivia is reading a book that is $1\frac{3}{8}$ inches thick. How many inches thicker is Tyree's book than Olivia's book?

Ⓐ $\frac{7}{8}$ inch

Ⓑ $\frac{3}{8}$ inch

Ⓒ $1\frac{1}{8}$ inches

Ⓓ $1\frac{3}{8}$ inches

6 The Willis Family ate $3\frac{4}{5}$ pizzas during a football game. The Miller Family ate $5\frac{3}{4}$ pizzas. Using the picture below, which equation represents the amount of pizza both families ate?

t = total amount

$3\frac{4}{5}$	$5\frac{3}{4}$

Ⓕ $t - 3\frac{4}{5} = 5\frac{3}{4}$

Ⓖ $3\frac{4}{5} + 5\frac{3}{4} = t$

Ⓗ $5\frac{3}{4} - 3\frac{4}{5} = t$

Ⓘ $t + 3\frac{4}{5} = 5\frac{3}{4}$

7 The Miami Marathon covers a distance of 26 miles 1,056 feet. How many feet is this?

1 mile = 5,280 feet

Ⓐ 6,336 feet

Ⓑ 27,456 feet

Ⓒ 137,280 feet

Ⓓ 138,336 feet

Go On

Name ____________________

8 An average-size adult Florida manatee measures 3 meters long. How many centimeters is this?

1 meter = 100 centimeters

9 An Asian elephant can eat about 10,500 pounds of food in one month. About how many tons can an Asian elephant eat in one month to the nearest ton?

Ⓕ 5 tons
Ⓖ 4 tons
Ⓗ 3 tons
Ⓘ 1 ton

1 ton = 2,000 pounds

10 The largest leatherback turtle on record was a male found on the west coast of Wales in 1988. He had a mass of 916 kilograms. What was his mass in grams?

Ⓐ 9,160,000 grams
Ⓑ 916,000 grams
Ⓒ 91,600 grams
Ⓓ 9,160 grams

1 kilogram = 1,000 grams

Go On

Name ______________________________

11 Explain which is a longer period of time, 120 months or 12 years.

1 year = 12 months

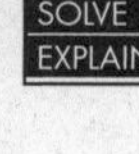

____

____

____

____

12 What is the length of the worm to the nearest $\frac{1}{4}$ inch?

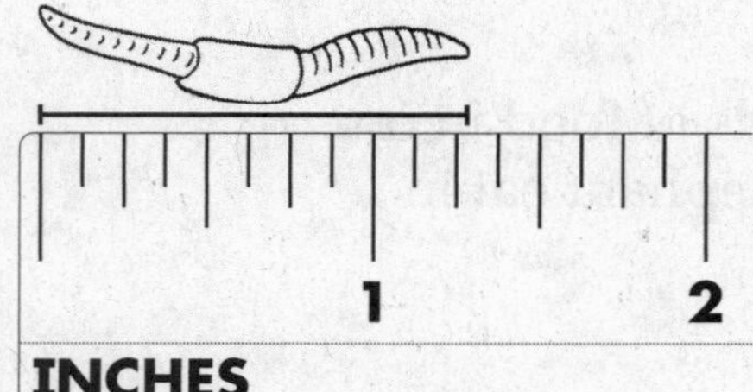

Ⓕ 1 inch

Ⓖ $1\frac{1}{4}$ inch

Ⓗ $1\frac{1}{2}$ inch

Ⓘ $1\frac{3}{4}$ inch

13 Which of the objects below measures 45 millimeters?

Ⓐ

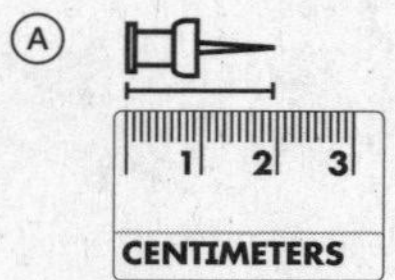

Ⓒ

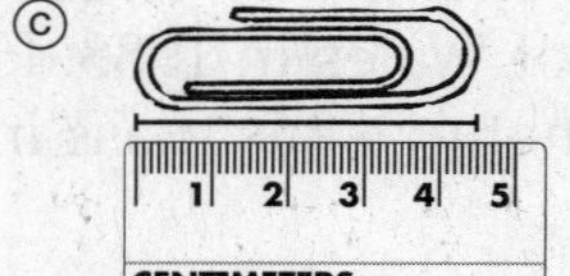

Ⓑ

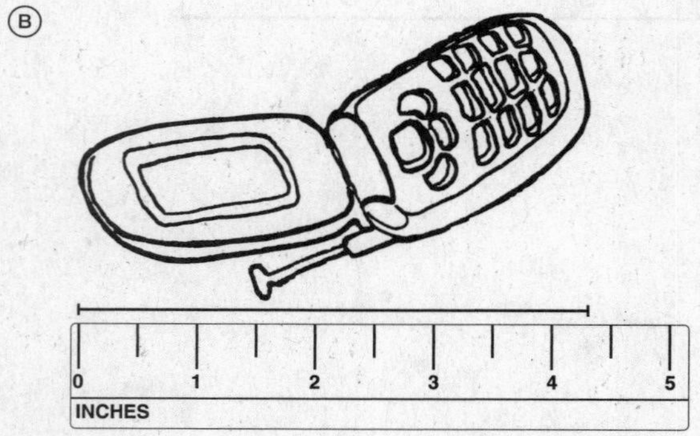

Ⓓ

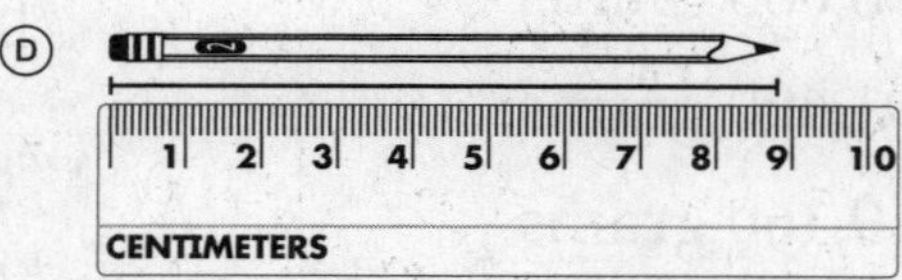

Go On

Name ______________________

14 Which unit would you use to best measure the weight of a bus?

Ⓕ Pounds
Ⓖ Ounces
Ⓗ Tons
Ⓘ Yards

15 What is a good estimate for the mass of a dollar bill?

Ⓐ 1 pound
Ⓑ 10 kilograms
Ⓒ 1 kilogram
Ⓓ 1 gram

16 What is the measure of the angle?

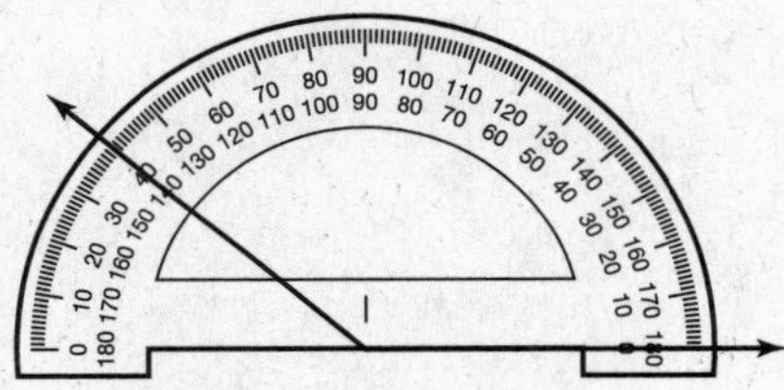

Ⓕ 40°
Ⓖ 50°
Ⓗ 130°
Ⓘ 140°

17 The area of Orlando is about the same as the area of the figure below. What is the area of the figure?

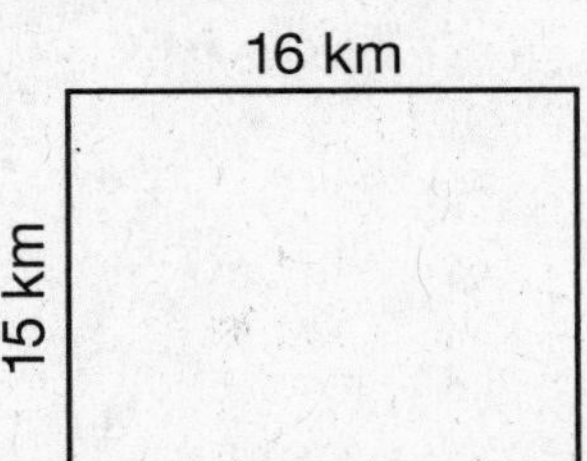

Area of rectangle = base × height

Ⓐ 62 km²
Ⓑ 96 km²
Ⓒ 240 km²
Ⓓ 256 km²

Name ______________________________

18 What is the area of the parallelogram?

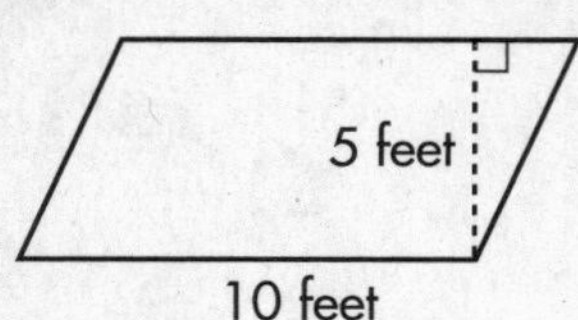

Area of parallelogram = base × height

Ⓕ 50 ft^2 Ⓗ 25 ft^2

Ⓖ 30 ft^2 Ⓘ 15 ft^2

19 What is the area of the triangular sail shown below?

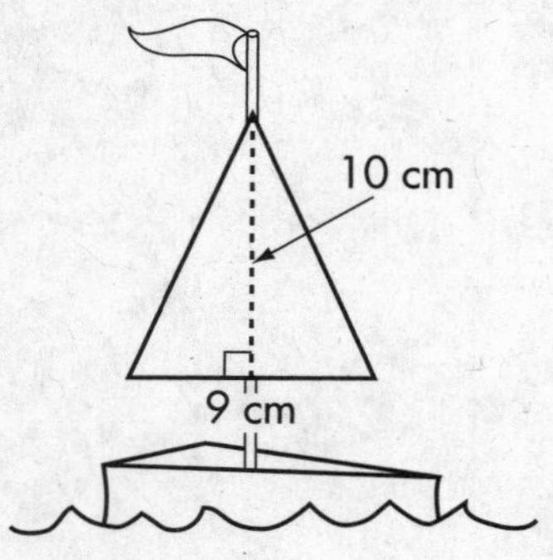

Area of triangle = $\frac{\text{base} \times \text{height}}{2}$

Ⓐ 90 cm^2 Ⓒ 45 cm^2

Ⓑ 55 cm^2 Ⓓ 19 cm^2

20 How many square feet is the area of a garden in the shape of a trapezoid with bases of 6 feet and 8 feet and a height of 7 feet?

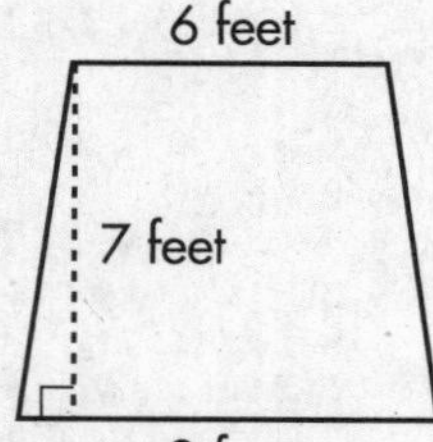

Area of trapezoid = $\frac{(\text{base 1} + \text{base 2})}{2}$ × height

0	0	0	0
1	1	1	1
2	2	2	2
3	3	3	3
4	4	4	4
5	5	5	5
6	6	6	6
7	7	7	7
8	8	8	8
9	9	9	9

Go On

Name ______________________

21 Zack's yard has the shape shown below. What is the area of Zack's yard?

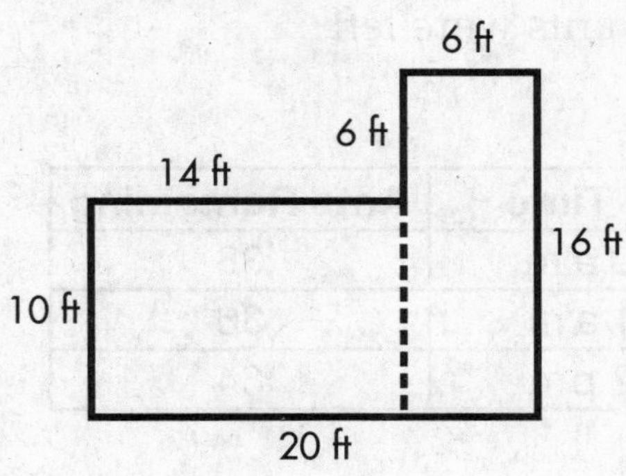

Area of rectangle = base × height

Ⓕ 320 ft^2　　Ⓗ 160 ft^2

Ⓖ 236 ft^2　　Ⓘ 140 ft^2

22 Rachel is making a blanket for her baby brother. She wants the blanket to have a perimeter of 14 feet and cover the greatest area possible. Draw pictures of all possible blankets with dimensions and make an organized list of their areas to help you find the dimensions of the blanket Rachel should make. Explain your answer.

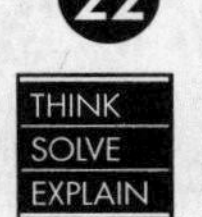

Pictures　　**List for Areas**

$6 \times 1 = 6$ ft^2

$5 \times 2 = 10$ ft^2

Area of rectangle = base × height

$4 \times 3 = 12$ ft^2

____

____

____

____

Go On

Name ______________________________

23 Stella noticed that 2 ants were escaping every half-hour from her ant farm. If she started with 38 ants at 10:00 A.M., which table would she use to find how many ants were left at 12:00 P.M.?

Ⓐ

Time	Ants Remaining
10 a.m	38
10:30 a.m	34
11 a.m	30
11:30 a.m	26
12 p.m	22

Ⓑ

Time	Ants Remaining
10 a.m	0
10:30 a.m	2
11 a.m	4
11:30 a.m	6
12 p.m	8

Ⓒ

Time	Ants Remaining
10 a.m	38
11 a.m	36
12 p.m	34

Ⓓ

Time	Ants Remaining
10 a.m	38
10:30 a.m	36
11 a.m	34
11:30 a.m	32
12 p.m	30

24 Which of the large square tiles can Avram use to completely cover his patio without cutting any tiles?

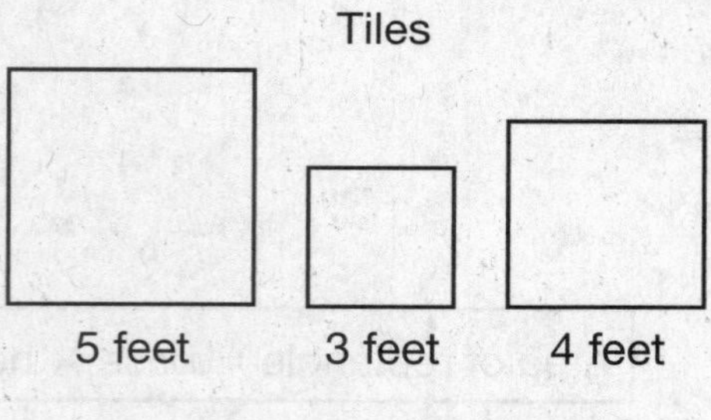

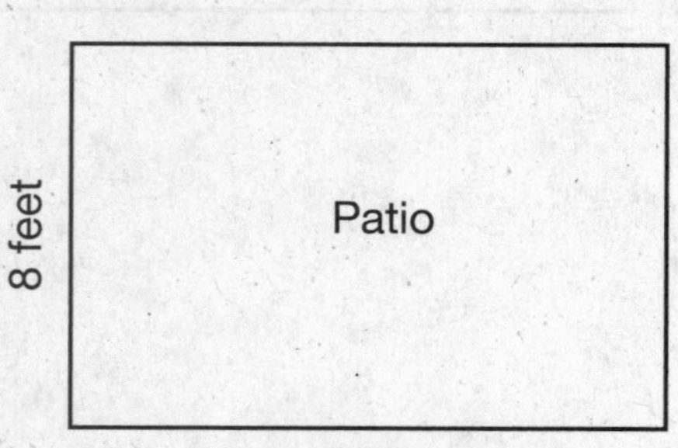

Ⓕ 3-foot and 5-foot tiles only

Ⓖ 5-foot tiles only

Ⓗ 4-foot tiles only

Ⓘ 3-foot tiles only

Name ____________________

Mark the best answer.

1 Which solid does the picture below resemble? (13-1)

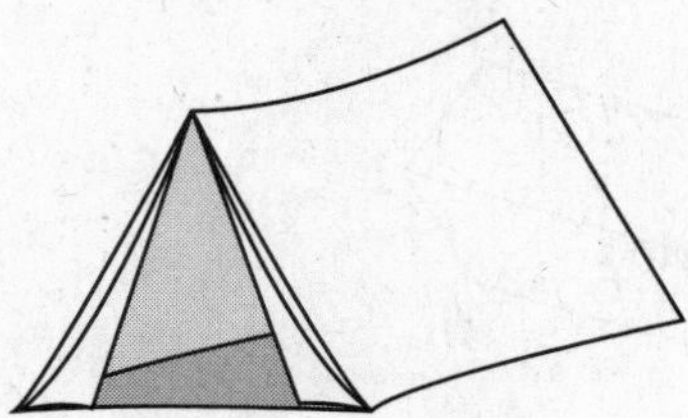

Ⓐ Prism
Ⓑ Pyramid
Ⓒ Cone
Ⓓ Cylinder

2 What solid can be made with the net shown? (13-3)

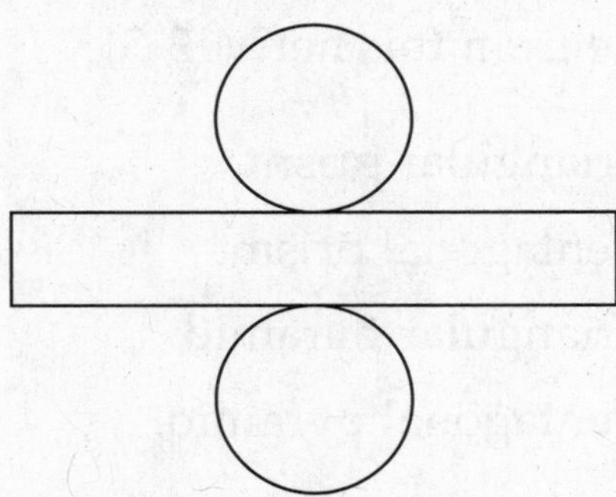

Ⓕ Cylinder
Ⓖ Cone
Ⓗ Sphere
Ⓘ Rectangular prism

3 Which names an edge of the polyhedron below? (13-2)

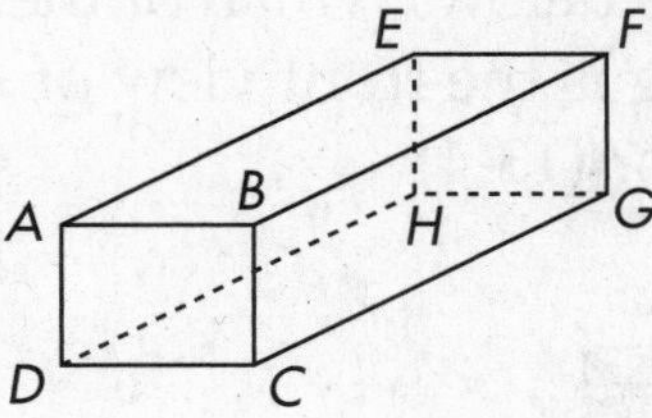

Ⓐ ▭*ABCD*
Ⓑ *F*
Ⓒ $\overline{BF}$
Ⓓ $\overline{AC}$

4 If office cubicles are arranged in a ring as shown with 4 units on each side, there are 12 cubicles in all. How many cubicles will there be if there are 5 units on each side? (13-5)

Ⓕ 10
Ⓖ 12
Ⓗ 16
Ⓘ 20

Go On

Topic 13
Florida Test

Name ______________________________

5 Lola stacked some cubes on the kitchen counter to make the sculpture below. Which of the following is the front view of the cubes? (13-4)

Ⓐ

Ⓑ

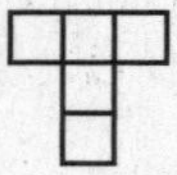

Ⓒ

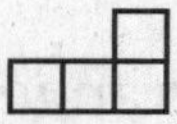

Ⓓ

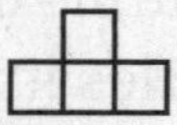

6 Maggie stacked some cubes as shown below. How many cubes are NOT visible? (13-4)

Ⓕ 0

Ⓖ 1

Ⓗ 2

Ⓘ 3

7 Which names a vertex in the pentagonal prism? (13-2)

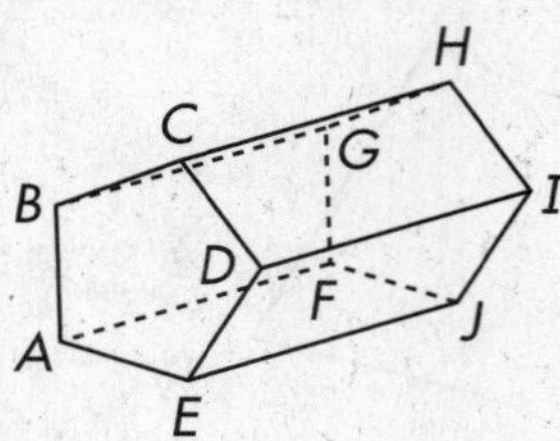

Ⓐ ⬠*FGHIJ*

Ⓑ *K*

Ⓒ *F*

Ⓓ $\overline{AB}$

8 A net has 5 triangles and 1 pentagon. What solid can be made from this net? (13-3)

Ⓕ Triangular prism

Ⓖ Pentagonal prism

Ⓗ Triangular pyramid

Ⓘ Pentagonal pyramid

Go On

Name ______________________________

9 Which names a face in the square pyramid? (13-2)

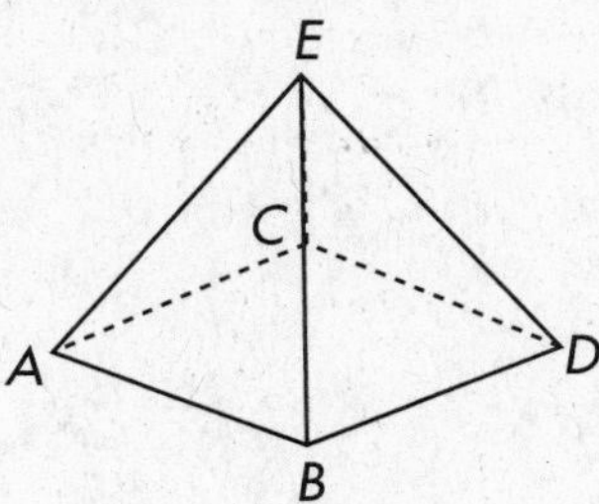

Ⓐ $\triangle CEA$

Ⓑ $\triangle BCA$

Ⓒ $\overline{ED}$

Ⓓ $\overline{CA}$

10 How many edges does a rectangular prism have? (13-1)

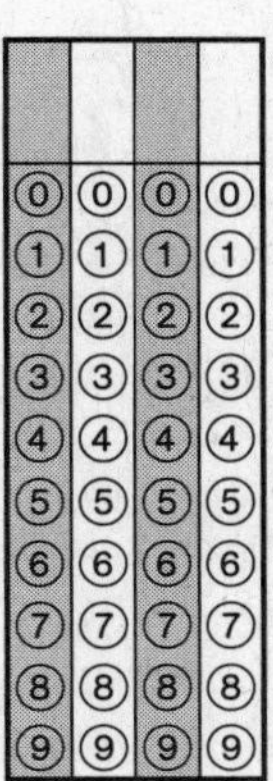

11 THINK SOLVE EXPLAIN Jenny cuts open her juice box along the edges and lays it flat to make a net. Draw the net that Jenny makes. (13-3)

STOP

Topic 13 Florida Test

Name ____________________

Mark the best answer.

1 The picture shows unit cubes in a stack. What is the volume of this rectangular prism? (14-3)

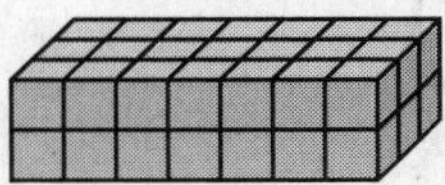

Ⓐ 42 cubic units

Ⓑ 36 cubic units

Ⓒ 24 cubic units

Ⓓ 21 cubic units

2 The figure below is made up of cubes and has a volume of 6 cm^3. What is the surface area of the solid figure? (14-6)

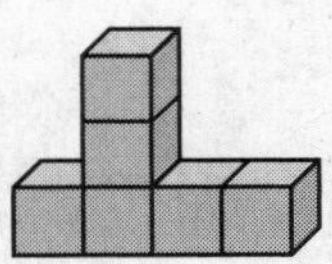

Ⓕ 6 cm^2

Ⓖ 24 cm^2

Ⓗ 26 cm^2

Ⓘ 36 cm^2

3 What is the volume of the stairs shown? (14-5)

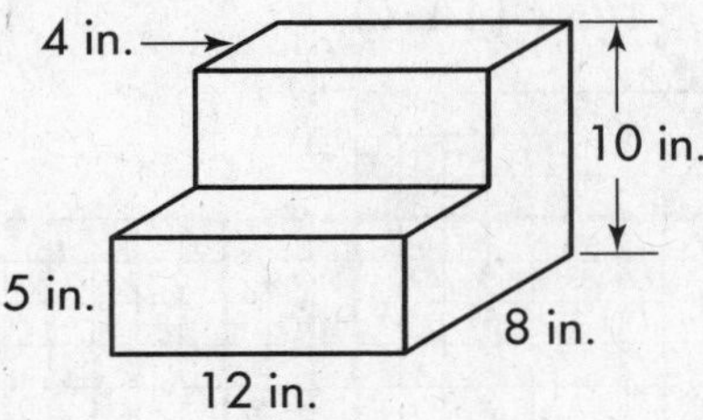

Ⓐ 960 in^3

Ⓑ 720 in^3

Ⓒ 480 in^3

Ⓓ 240 in^3

4 What is the surface area of the cube formed by the net shown? (14-2)

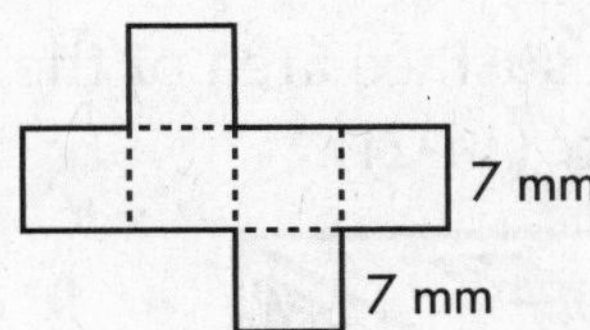

Ⓕ 196 mm^2

Ⓖ 294 mm^2

Ⓗ 343 mm^2

Ⓘ 490 mm^2

Go On

5 How many square units is the surface area of the prism formed by this net? (14-1)

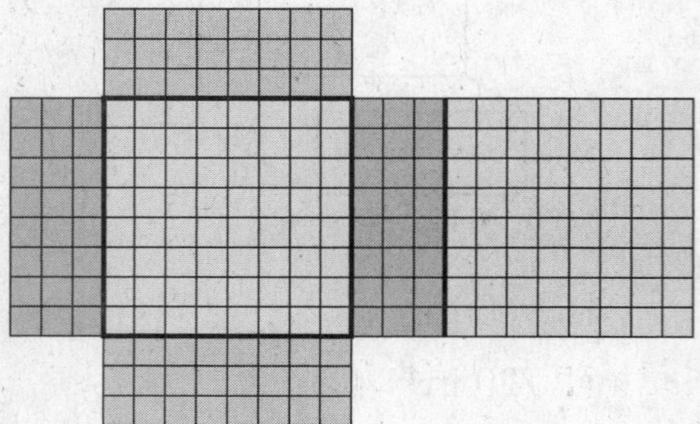

Ⓐ 112 square units

Ⓑ 192 square units

Ⓒ 224 square units

Ⓓ 448 square units

6 What is the surface area of the jewelry box? (14-2)

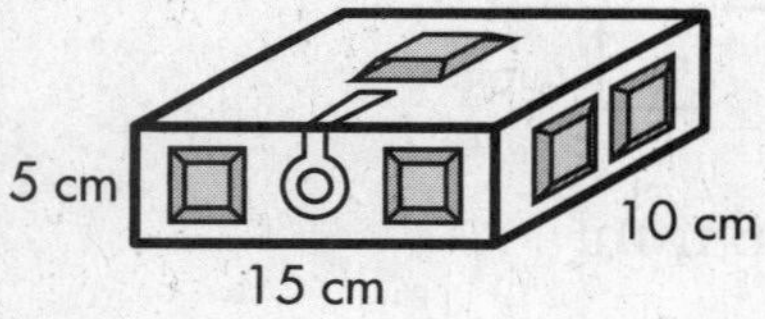

Ⓕ 750 cm^2

Ⓖ 650 cm^2

Ⓗ 550 cm^2

Ⓘ 450 cm^2

7 What is the volume of the trunk? (14-4)

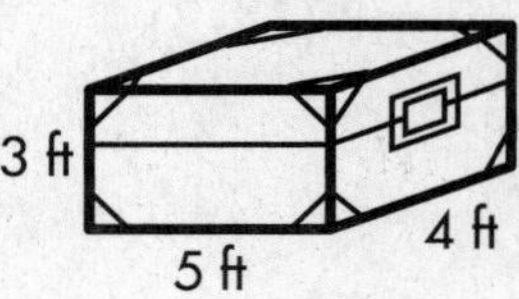

Ⓐ 12 ft^3

Ⓑ 24 ft^3

Ⓒ 30 ft^3

Ⓓ 60 ft^3

8 The rectangular prism below is made from cubes that each measure 1 cubic centimeter. What is the volume of the prism? (14-3)

Ⓕ 9 cm^3

Ⓖ 12 cm^3

Ⓗ 18 cm^3

Ⓘ 24 cm^3

Go On

Name ______________________________

9 Which packing carton has a volume of 24 cubic inches? (14-4)

Ⓐ
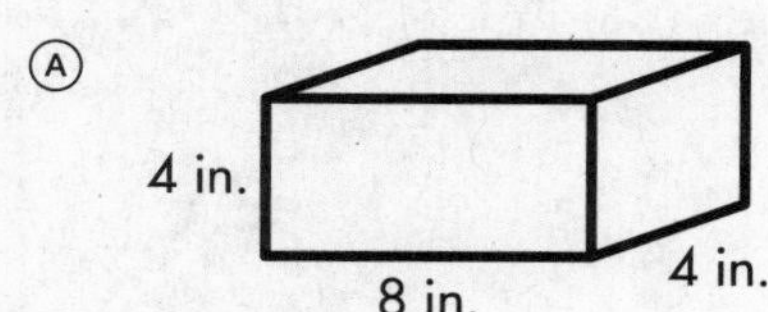

Ⓑ
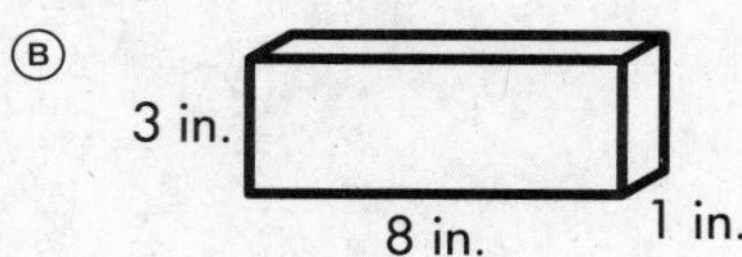

Ⓒ
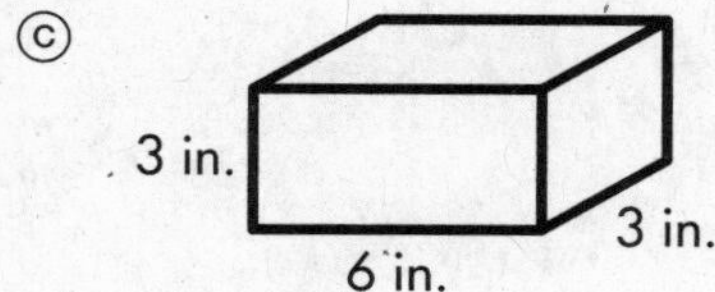

Ⓓ
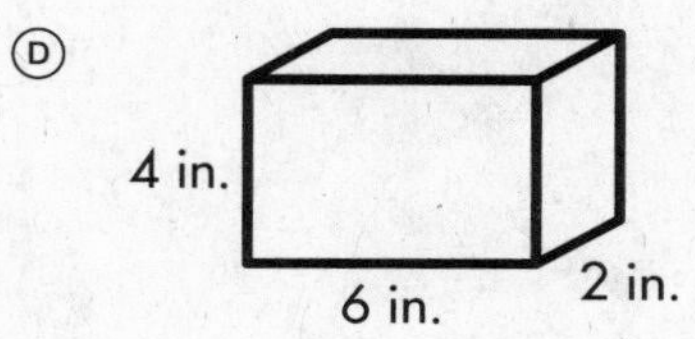

10 Caroline's cube has an edge that measures 2 centimeters. Dimitri's cube has an edge that measures 4 centimeters. How many more cubic centimeters is the volume of Dimitri's cube than Caroline's cube? (14-4)

11 THINK SOLVE EXPLAIN The solid figure below is made up of unit cubes. Explain how you can use objects or reasoning to find the volume of this solid figure. (14-6)

____
____
____
____
____
____
____
____
____
____
____
____
____

STOP

Name ____________________

1 The graph shows the different kinds of doctors who work at a hospital.

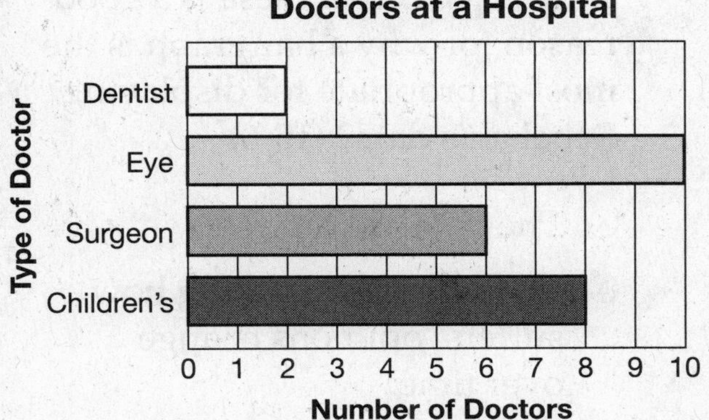

Which is NOT true about the graph that is shown? (15-1)

Ⓐ The data show changes over time.
Ⓑ The displayed data can be counted.
Ⓒ The interval of number of doctors is 1.
Ⓓ The data are discrete.

2 Between which times did the temperature decrease? (15-4)

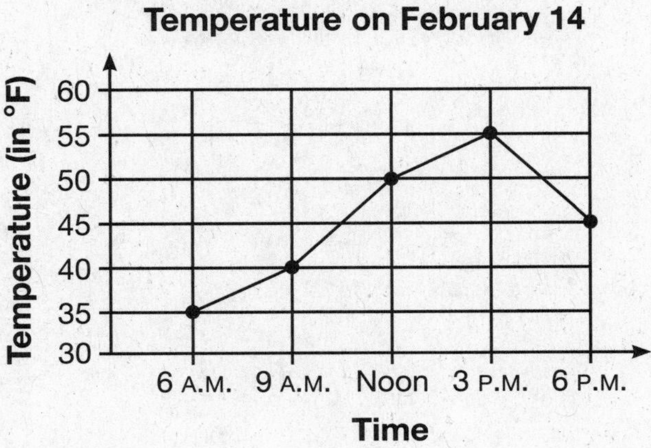

Ⓕ Between 6 A.M and 9 A.M.
Ⓖ Between 9 A.M and noon
Ⓗ Between noon and 3 P.M.
Ⓘ Between 3 P.M and 6 P.M.

3 Rico did a study on the total number of hurricanes that hit the U.S. by the end of each year between 2000 and 2008. What would be the most appropriate type of graph to use to display Rico's data? (15-6)

Ⓐ Bar graph
Ⓑ Picture graph
Ⓒ Line graph
Ⓓ Double-bar graph

4 The Digi-Tunes Company makes MP3 players. The table shows the number of units sold each year.

MP3 Player Sales

Year	2006	2007	2008	2009
Number of Units Sold	100	80	60	40

If you want to use the table to complete the line graph below, which of these is NOT an appropriate step? (15-5)

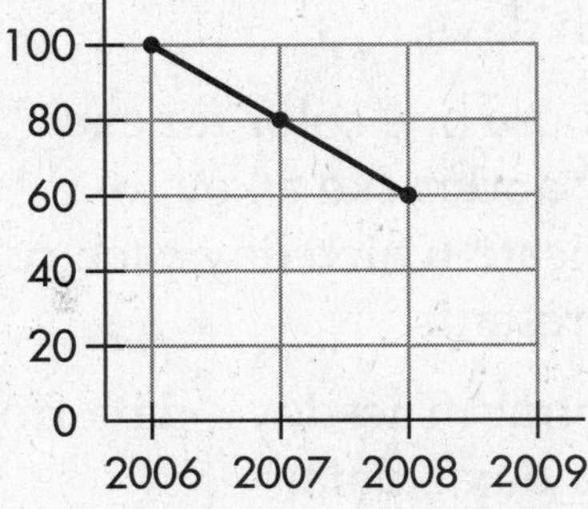

Ⓕ Add a title to the graph.
Ⓖ Label the vertical axis "Year."
Ⓗ Plot a point for 2009 and connect it to the point for 2008.
Ⓘ Label the vertical axis "Number of Units Sold."

Go On

5 The graphs below show the number of times each roller coaster was operated on two different days.

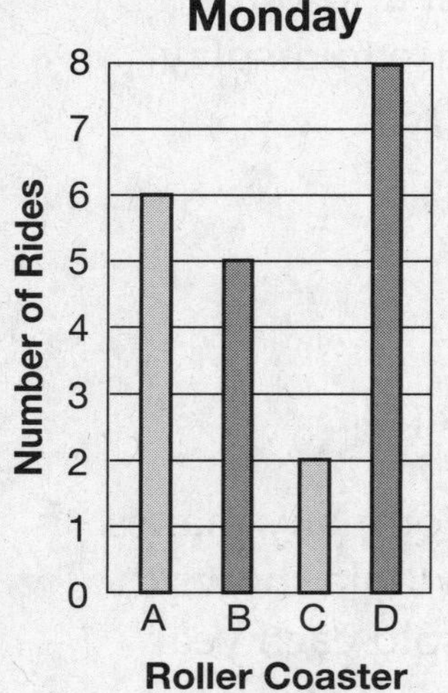

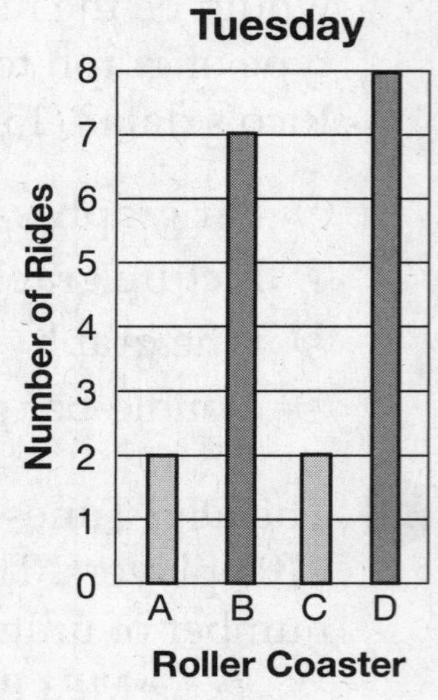

The theme park owner wants to make a double-bar graph based on each of these graphs to compare the data more efficiently. Which of the following describes one of the steps to do this? (15-3)

Ⓐ Find the total number of rides for Roller Coaster D for both days.

Ⓑ Choose one color for each day and make a key to indicate which day each color represents.

Ⓒ Subtract Tuesday's data from Monday's data.

Ⓓ Double the scale on the vertical axis.

6 Rebekah conducted a survey to find out what the most popular surfing destination is among local surfers. Which of these is a good reason for why a bar graph is the most appropriate for displaying Rebekah's data? (15-6)

Ⓐ The data are discrete.

Ⓑ Rebekah is comparing how surfers' opinions change over time.

Ⓒ The popularity of a surfing destination changes from year to year.

Ⓓ The data are continuous.

Go On

Name ______________________________

7 Callie and Paige live on opposite sides of the country and wanted to know if students preferred different weather based on where they lived. Each girl surveyed 100 students at her school. The graph below compares their findings.

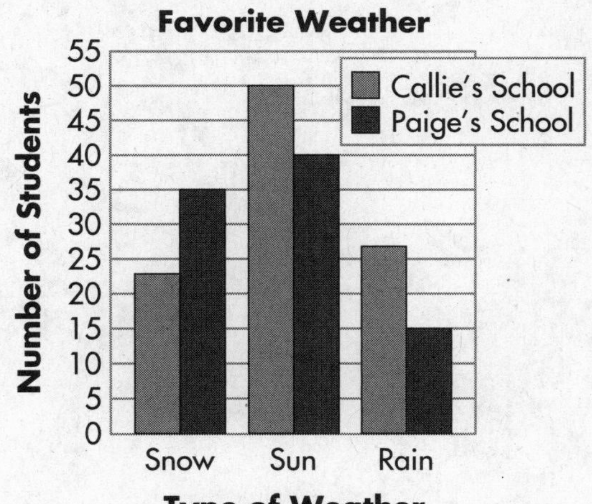

How many more students preferred sun at Callie's school than at Paige's school? (15-2)

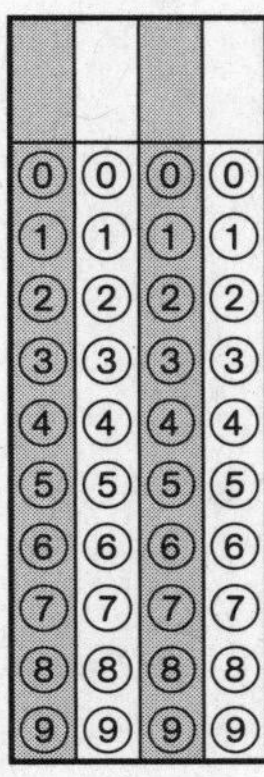

8 THINK SOLVE EXPLAIN The graph below shows the population of Bigtown between 2000 and 2008.

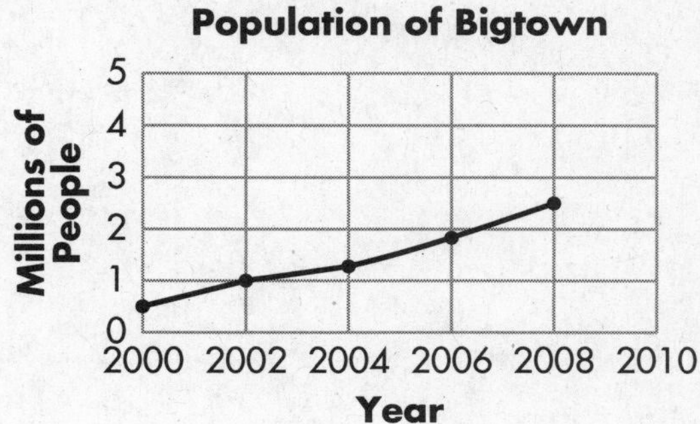

How can this graph be used to help explain why 3,000,000 people is a good prediction for Bigtown's population in 2010? (15-7)

____

____

____

____

____

____

____

____

____

STOP

Topic 15 Florida Test

Name ______________________

1 Hawaii is the only state to have a record low temperature that is above zero. The lowest recorded temperature in Hawaii was $^{+}12$°F. What is the opposite of $^{+}12$? (16-1)

Ⓐ 12

Ⓑ $^{+}11$

Ⓒ $^{-}12$

Ⓓ $^{-}24$

2 The elevations of different points in the United States are given in the table. These elevations are measured by using sea level as 0.

Location	Elevation (meters)
Eagle Mountain	$^{+}702$
Colorado River	$^{+}21$
New Orleans	$^{-}2$
Long Island Sound	0

Which of the following lists the elevations from *least* to *greatest*? (16-3)

Ⓕ 0, $^{-}2$, $^{+}21$, $^{+}702$

Ⓖ $^{+}702$, $^{+}21$, $^{-}2$, 0

Ⓗ –2, 0, $^{+}702$, $^{+}21$

Ⓘ $^{-}2$, 0, $^{+}21$, $^{+}702$

3 What is the distance between $^{-}5$ and $^{+}4$ on a number line? (16-4)

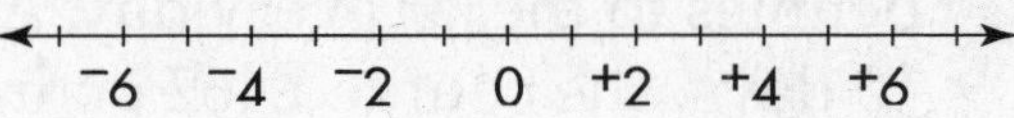

Ⓐ 1 unit

Ⓑ 5 units

Ⓒ 8 units

Ⓓ 9 units

4 Which of the following can be used to represent adding 4 pounds to a balance scale? (16-1)

Ⓕ $^{+}8$

Ⓖ $^{+}4$

Ⓗ $^{-}4$

Ⓘ $^{+}16$

5 Which comparison is true? (16-3)

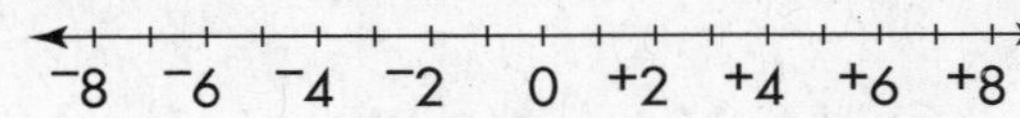

Ⓐ $^{-}7 > {}^{-}2$

Ⓑ $0 < {}^{-}1$

Ⓒ $^{+}3 < {}^{-}3$

Ⓓ $^{-}2 > {}^{-}7$

Go On

6 Heather's father gave her a jar of pennies. She decided to add 3 pennies to the jar every day. After 10 days, she counted 462 pennies in all. How many pennies were in the jar before Heather began adding pennies? (16-5)

Ⓕ 432

Ⓖ 492

Ⓗ 1,386

Ⓘ 4,620

7 What is the integer at Point *E*? (16-1)

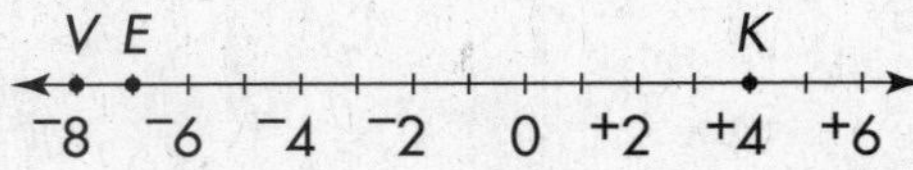

Ⓐ $^-8$

Ⓑ $^-7$

Ⓒ $^+1$

Ⓓ $^+4$

8 Which number line shows a graph of Point *Q* at $^+1$? (16-2)

Ⓕ Q — 0 $^+2$ $^+4$ $^+6$ $^+8$ $^+10$

Ⓖ Q — $^-4$ $^-2$ 0 $^+2$ $^+4$ $^+6$

Ⓗ Q — $^-4$ $^-2$ 0 $^+2$ $^+4$ $^+6$

Ⓘ Q — $^-4$ $^-2$ 0 $^+2$ $^+4$ $^+6$

9 What is the distance between Point *W* and Point *X*? (16-4)

W X — $^-4$ $^-2$ 0 $^+2$

Ⓐ 2 units

Ⓑ 1 unit

Ⓒ 0 units

Ⓓ $^-2$ units

10 Which description could be used for the integer $^-12$? (16-1)

Ⓕ Adding \$12 to your bank account

Ⓖ 12° below 0

Ⓗ A gain of 12 yards

Ⓘ 12 feet above sea level

11 Which shows the integers in order from *greatest* to *least*? (16-3)

Ⓐ 0, $^-4$, $^-6$, $^-18$

Ⓑ $^-4$, $^-6$, 0, $^-18$

Ⓒ $^-18$, $^-6$, $^-4$, 0

Ⓓ $^-18$, 0, $^-4$, $^-6$

Go On

Name ______________________________

12 Which number line is a graph of the following integers? (16-2)

0, $^-5$, $^+15$, $^+20$, $^-10$

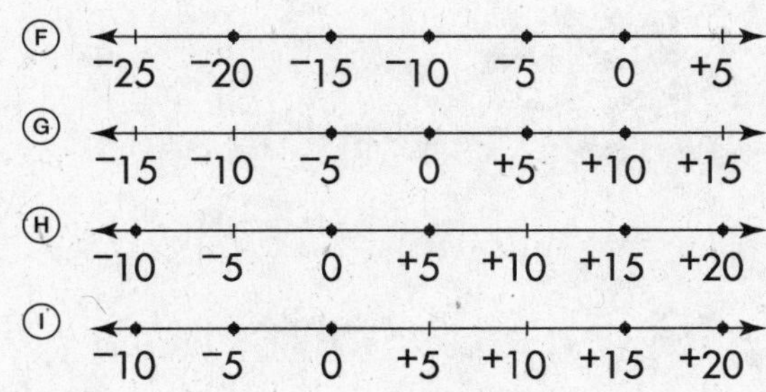

13 Which two integers are 4 units from $^-3$ on a number line? (16-4)

(A) $^+7$ and $^+1$

(B) $^+1$ and $^+7$

(C) $^-7$ and $^+1$

(D) $^-2$ and $^+7$

14 What is the distance, in units, between $^-9$ and $^+9$ on a number line? (16-4)

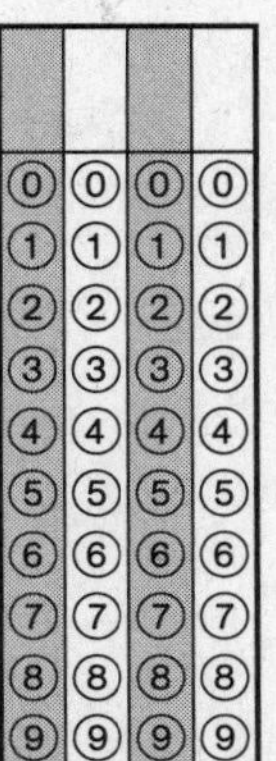

15 THINK SOLVE EXPLAIN

Milly was flying a kite a certain height above the ground. First, the kite dropped down 14 feet. Then a gust of wind blew the kite upward 23 feet. The wind died down and the kite dropped 46 feet to the ground. At what height was the kite before it dropped the first time? Describe what you did to find the answer. (16-5)

____

____

____

____

____

____

____

STOP

Name ______________________________

1 Jacob and his uncle were going on a bike ride. They wanted to bike across the park and then on to the school. Before they started biking, Jacob planned their route on the map below.

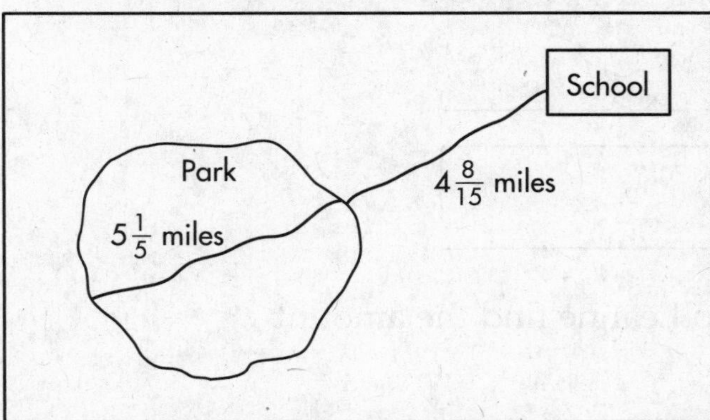

What is the total distance they planned to ride their bikes?

Ⓐ $9\frac{1}{5}$ miles

Ⓑ $9\frac{9}{15}$ miles

Ⓒ $9\frac{11}{15}$ miles

Ⓓ $10\frac{3}{5}$ miles

2 What is the most appropriate unit to measure the mass of the eraser shown below?

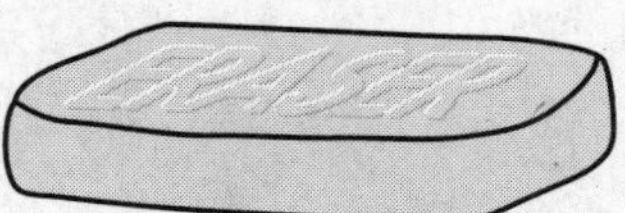

Ⓕ Pound

Ⓖ Liter

Ⓗ Gram

Ⓘ Kilogram

Go On

3 Leanne cut a piece of cloth $6\frac{4}{7}$ yards long from a roll of cloth that was $18\frac{1}{2}$ yards long. Leanne drew the picture below to find how much cloth is left on the roll.

$18\frac{1}{2}$ yards

$6\frac{4}{7}$ yards	***x***

Which equation would NOT help Leanne find the amount of cloth left on the roll?

Ⓐ $18\frac{1}{2} + 6\frac{4}{7} = x$

Ⓑ $6\frac{4}{7} + x = 18\frac{1}{2}$

Ⓒ $18\frac{1}{2} - 6\frac{4}{7} = x$

Ⓓ $18\frac{1}{2} - x = 6\frac{4}{7}$

4 The dimensions of the clock at a sports stadium are shown below.

14 feet

14 feet

Area = base × height

What is the area of the clock?

Ⓕ 298 square feet

Ⓖ 196 square feet

Ⓗ 96 square feet

Ⓘ 28 square feet

Go On

5 Zack's family is having a picnic. They put 2 picnic tables together as shown below.

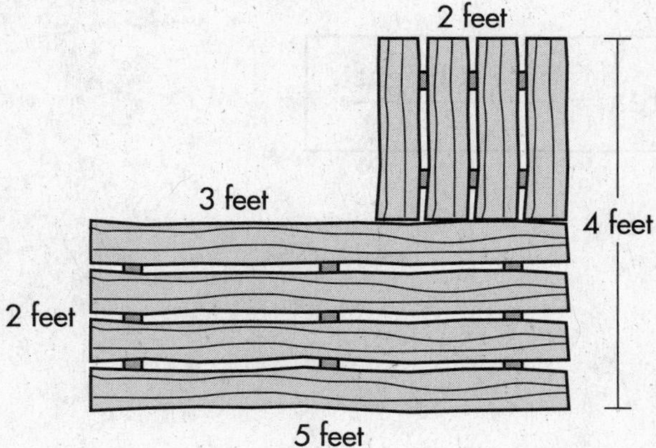

How many square feet is the total combined area of the picnic tables?

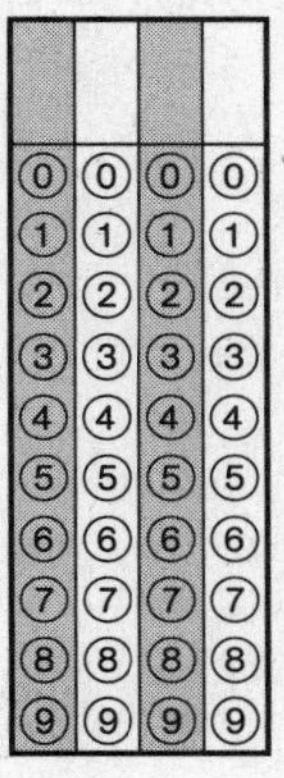

6 What is the greatest common factor of 12 and 18?

Ⓐ 2

Ⓑ 6

Ⓒ 9

Ⓓ 30

Go On

7 Mr. Kline printed his address number on a reflective sign shaped like the one shown below.

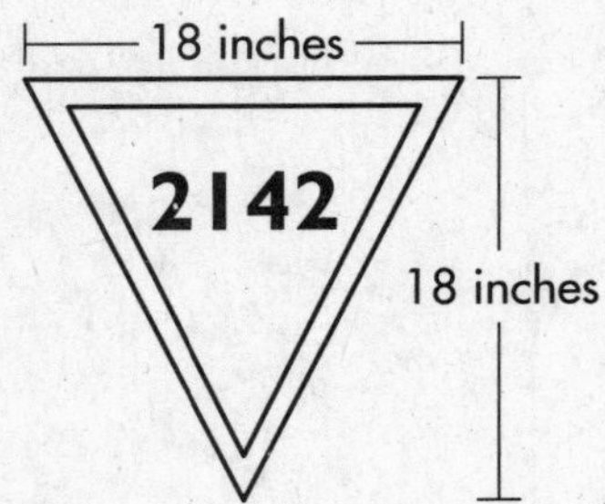

$$\text{Area} = \frac{\text{base} \times \text{height}}{2}$$

What is the area of Mr. Kline's sign?

Ⓕ 324 square inches

Ⓖ 162 square inches

Ⓗ 54 square inches

Ⓘ 36 square inches

8 The record high temperature for Gainesville, Florida, was 103°F. What is the opposite of $^{+}103$?

Ⓐ $^{+}109$

Ⓑ $^{+}103$

Ⓒ $^{-}103$

Ⓓ $^{-}107$

Go On

Name ______________________________

9 According to the Florida Fish and Wildlife Conservation Commission, the Florida state record for the length of an alligator is $14\frac{5}{8}$ feet. The Everglades National Park lists the largest alligator ever recorded in Florida at $17\frac{5}{12}$ feet long. What is the difference in their lengths?

Ⓕ $2\frac{3}{4}$ feet

Ⓖ $2\frac{19}{24}$ feet

Ⓗ $3\frac{5}{8}$ feet

Ⓘ $3\frac{5}{6}$ feet

10 Which of the following is closest to the measure of the angle shown below?

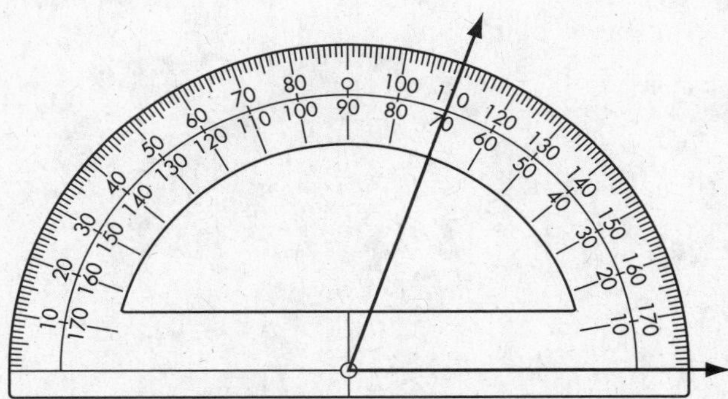

Ⓐ 120°

Ⓑ 110°

Ⓒ 80°

Ⓓ 70°

Go On

Name ______________________

11 Which solid has the number of vertices, edges, and faces listed in the table below?

Vertices	Edges	Faces
8	12	6

Ⓕ

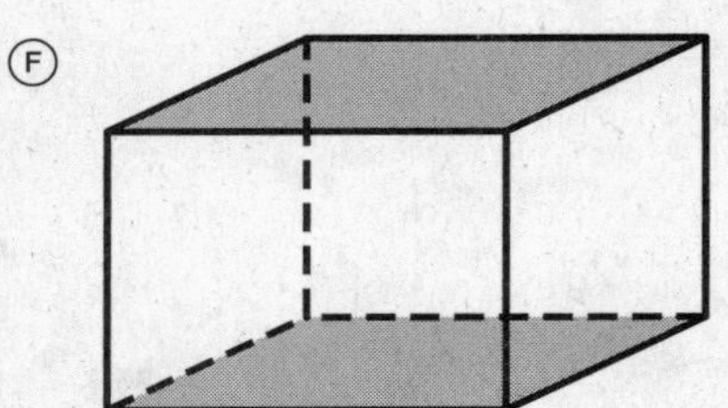

Ⓖ

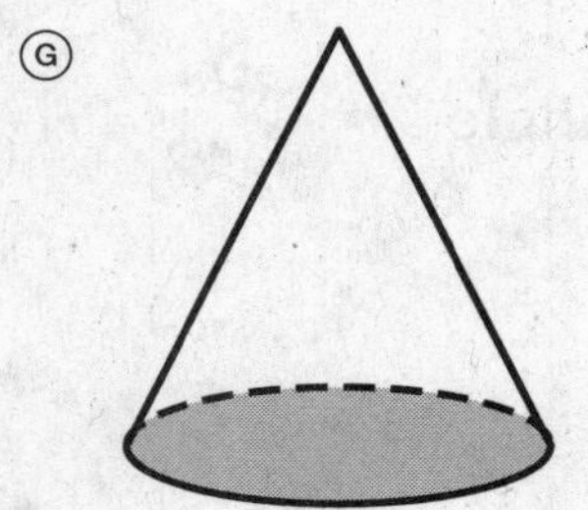

Ⓗ

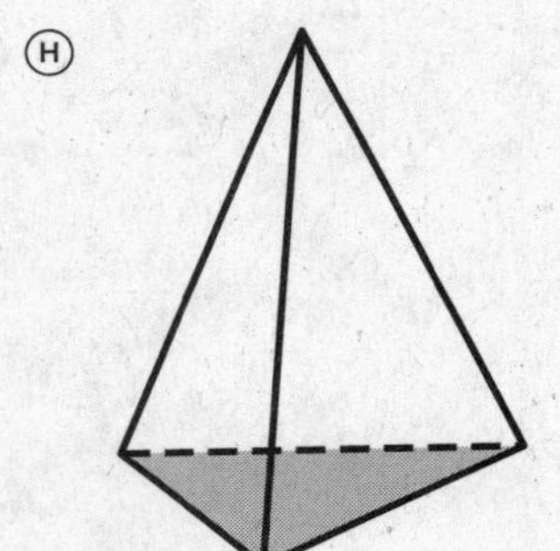

Ⓘ

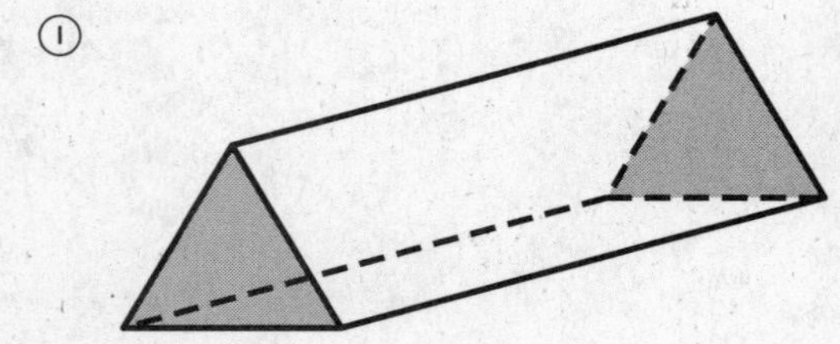

Go On

Name ______________________

12 The students in Ms. London's class took a survey on their favorite subject. The data from the survey are shown below.

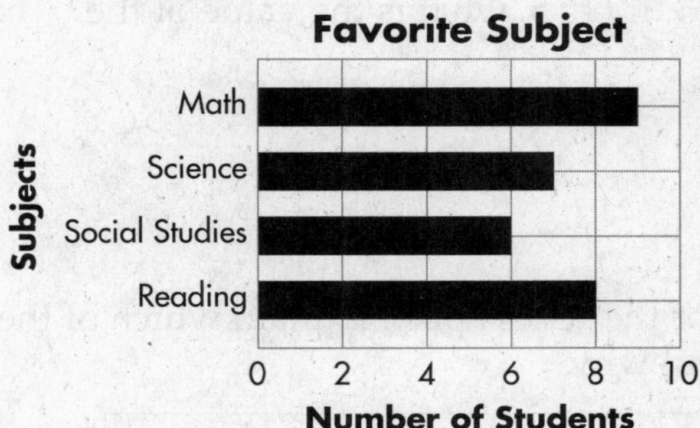

How many more students like math than science?

Ⓐ 1

Ⓑ 2

Ⓒ 6

Ⓓ 9

13 Which solid can be made from the net shown below?

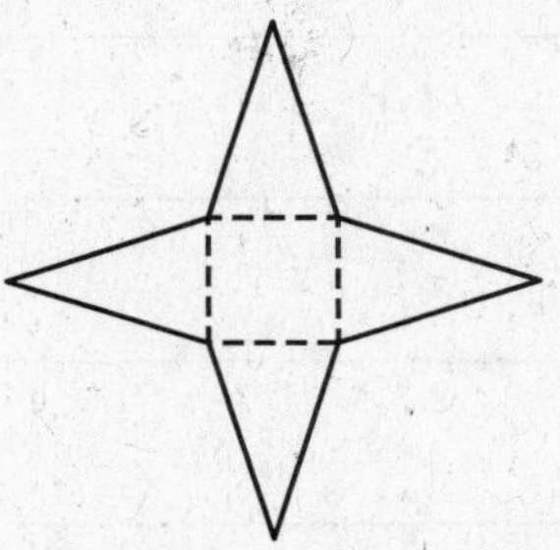

Ⓕ Pyramid

Ⓖ Cylinder

Ⓗ Rectangle

Ⓘ Prism

Go On

Name ______________________________

14 Mr. Garcia and his 30 students are collecting soup labels to help buy classroom equipment. The total number of labels collected can be found by evaluating the expression $30l + 15$. If $l = 5$, what is the value of the expression?

Ⓐ 75
Ⓑ 150
Ⓒ 165
Ⓓ 320

15 Jackie is painting boxes to be used for the school play. Explain which of the boxes below will need more paint and why.

Surface Area (SA) (polyhedron) = the sum of the area of all faces

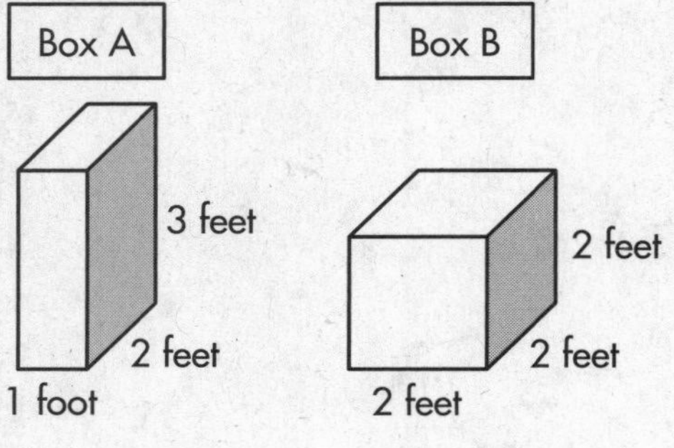

____

____

____

____

____

____

____

____

____

Go On

Name ____________________

16 Mr. Musial traveled by car to a destination that is 1,150 miles from his home. It took him 3 days to drive to this destination. If Mr. Musial traveled the same distance each day, about how many miles did he travel each day? Use estimation.

Ⓕ 600 miles

Ⓖ 500 miles

Ⓗ 400 miles

Ⓘ 300 miles

17 Kumar went to the Florida Aquarium with his class on Tuesday. He learned that a mature giant octopus has a total of 2,240 suckers on all of its arms.

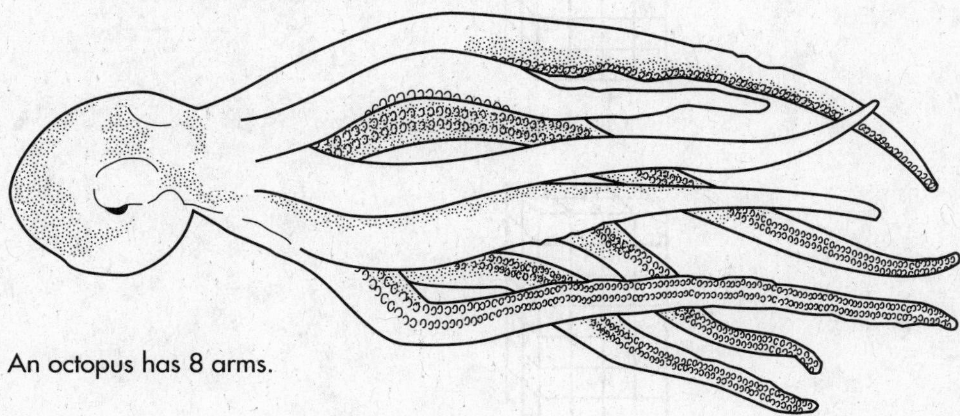

An octopus has 8 arms.

If there are an equal number of suckers on each arm, how many suckers are on each arm?

0	0	0	0
1	1	1	1
2	2	2	2
3	3	3	3
4	4	4	4
5	5	5	5
6	6	6	6
7	7	7	7
8	8	8	8
9	9	9	9

Go On

18 Some hummingbirds can flap their wings 1,600 times in 20 seconds. How many flaps can these hummingbirds flap their wings each second?

Ⓐ 8,000

Ⓑ 800

Ⓒ 80

Ⓓ 8

19 Raul built these models out of unit cubes. Which model has the greatest volume?

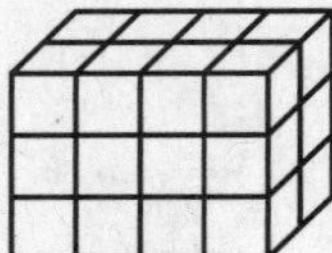

Model A

Model C

Model B

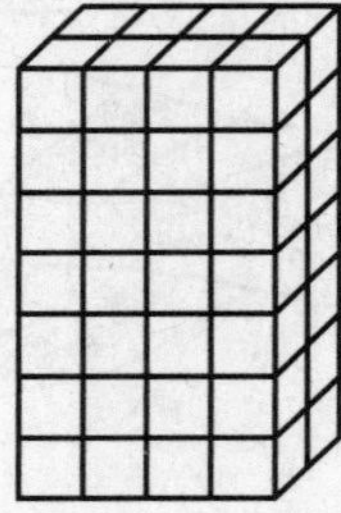

Model D

Ⓕ Model A

Ⓖ Model B

Ⓗ Model C

Ⓘ Model D

Name ______________________________

20 Below is a map showing some of Tad's favorite places in his town.

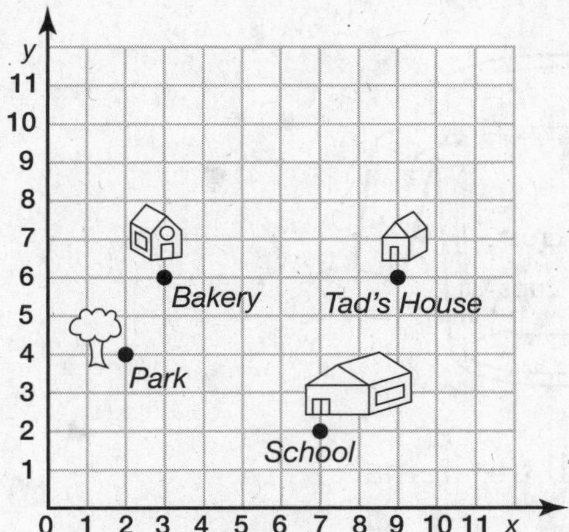

How many horizontal blocks separate Tad's house from the bakery?

Ⓐ 0

Ⓑ 4

Ⓒ 6

Ⓓ 7

21 The leg of an average human has a femur, or thigh bone, that is 48 centimeters long. What is this length in millimeters?

1 centimeter = 10 millimeters

Ⓕ 48 millimeters

Ⓖ 480 millimeters

Ⓗ 1,480 millimeters

Ⓘ 14,800 millimeters

Go On

22 Carla is planning to bake a cake, a batch of cookies, and a pie that calls for the following amounts of flour.

How much flour does Carla need to bake all the items?

Ⓐ $4\frac{4}{5}$ cups

Ⓑ $5\frac{5}{8}$ cups

Ⓒ $6\frac{1}{8}$ cups

Ⓓ $6\frac{7}{24}$ cups

23 The average temperature of a dog or cat is about 101°F. The average human body temperature is 98.6°F. What is the difference in the temperatures?

Ⓕ 3.4°F

Ⓖ 2.4°F

Ⓗ 1.4°F

Ⓘ 0.14°F

Go On

24 What is the most appropriate unit to measure the weight of a box of paper clips?

Ⓐ Pound

Ⓑ Ounce

Ⓒ Ton

Ⓓ Kilogram

25 Julie used the grids below to model the addition of two numbers.

Which sum is represented by Julie's model?

Ⓕ 2.00 + 0.06

Ⓖ 1.00 + 0.47

Ⓗ 1.06 + 0.47

Ⓘ 1.47 + 0.60

Go On

26 The nutrition label on the jar of peanut butter below shows the amount of protein in one serving of peanut butter.

How many milligrams of protein are in one serving of peanut butter?

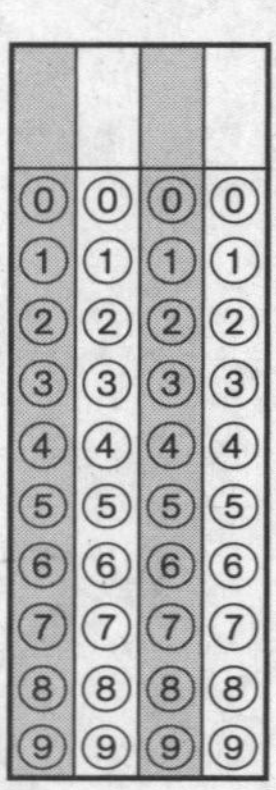

1 gram = 1,000 milligrams

27 Kevin's grandmother made a quilt for him out of pieces of cloth shaped like the trapezoid below.

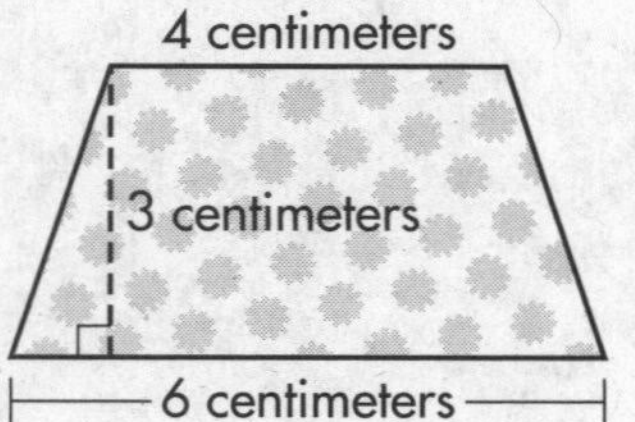

What is the area of each piece of cloth?

Ⓐ 15 square centimeters

Ⓑ 18 square centimeters

Ⓒ 24 square centimeters

Ⓓ 72 square centimeters

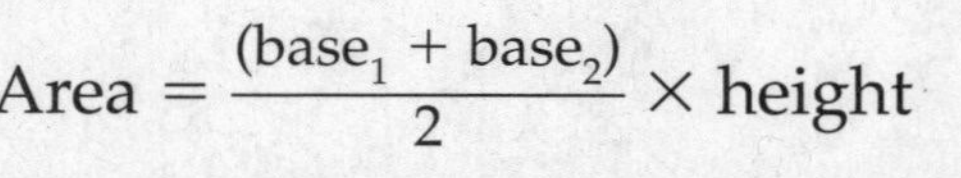

$$\text{Area} = \frac{(\text{base}_1 + \text{base}_2)}{2} \times \text{height}$$

Go On

Name ______________________________

28 The fastest nonstop flight around the Earth by a pilot flying alone took about 77 hours. The pilot traveled a distance of 26,389 miles. Using compatible numbers, what is the best way to estimate the number of miles the pilot flew each hour?

Ⓕ 26,389 ÷ 80

Ⓖ 24,000 ÷ 80

Ⓗ 26,000 ÷ 80

Ⓘ 27,000 ÷ 70

29 Which line segment measures about $1\frac{1}{4}$ inches long?

Ⓐ 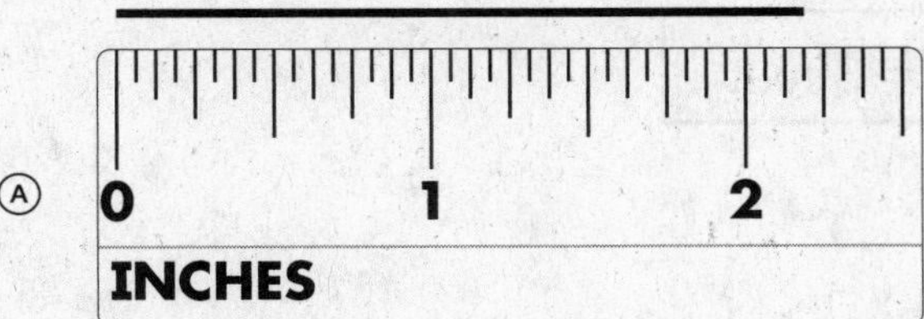

Ⓑ 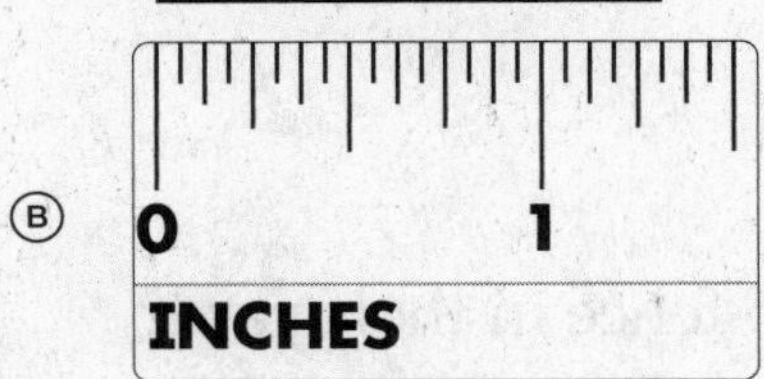

Ⓒ 

Ⓓ 0 1 2
INCHES

End-of-Year Test
Topics **1–16**

Go On

Name ___________________________

30 A hockey team played 9 home games. The same number of people came to each game. If 18,000 people came to all the games, how many people came to each game?

Ⓕ 20

Ⓖ 200

Ⓗ 2,000

Ⓘ 20,000

31 The Smiths are putting wood fencing around their yard. The dimensions of their yard are shown below.

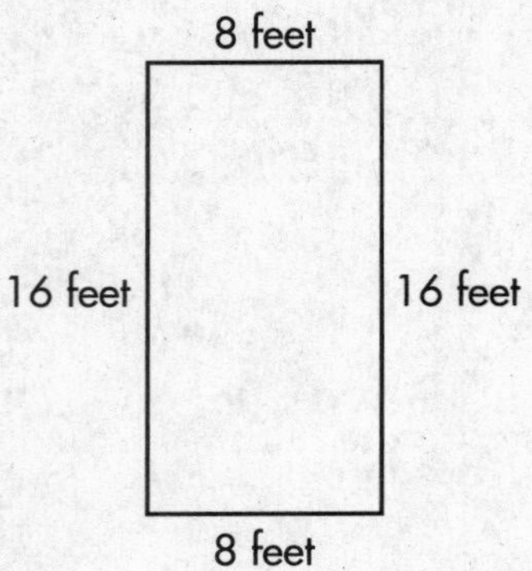

1 yard = 3 feet

How many yards of fencing do the Smiths need to fence in their yard?

0	0	0	0
1	1	1	1
2	2	2	2
3	3	3	3
4	4	4	4
5	5	5	5
6	6	6	6
7	7	7	7
8	8	8	8
9	9	9	9

Go On

Name ____________________

32 The table below shows the finish times of riders at the Great Trail Bicycle Race. Jan wants to determine how many minutes she finished before Carlos. Which information in the table is extra information?

Great Trail Bicycle Race Finish Times		
Rider	**Finish Time**	**Average Speed**
Jan	1 hour 50 minutes	8.75 mph
Brent	1 hour 40 minutes	9.6 mph
Carlos	2 hours 2 minutes	7.9 mph

Ⓐ Carlos's finish time.

Ⓑ Brent's finish time.

Ⓒ Jan's finish time.

Ⓓ 1 hour 50 minutes

33 The lengths of Steve's and Jim's model trains are shown below.

Steve's train

14.82 centimeters

Jim's train

11.16 centimeters

Which is the best estimate of the difference in length of the trains?

Ⓕ 1 centimeter

Ⓖ 2 centimeters

Ⓗ 4 centimeters

Ⓘ 6 centimeters

Go On

34 The table below shows the number of new customers at a department store. Which graph correctly displays the data in the table?

Number of New Customers per Hour	
Hour	**Number of New Customers**
9 A.M.	30
10 A.M.	34
11 P.M.	38
12 P.M.	46

Ⓐ
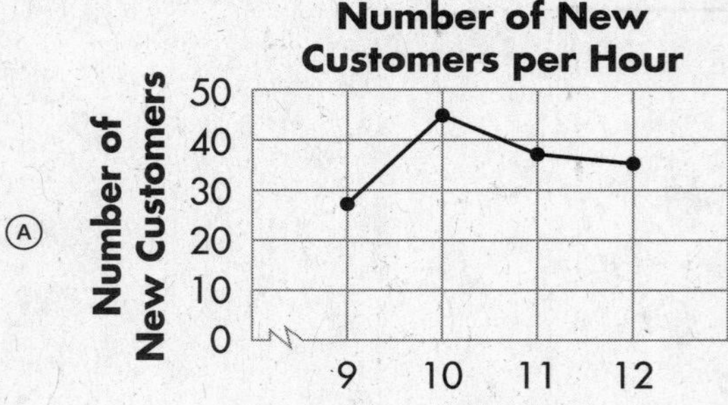

Ⓑ
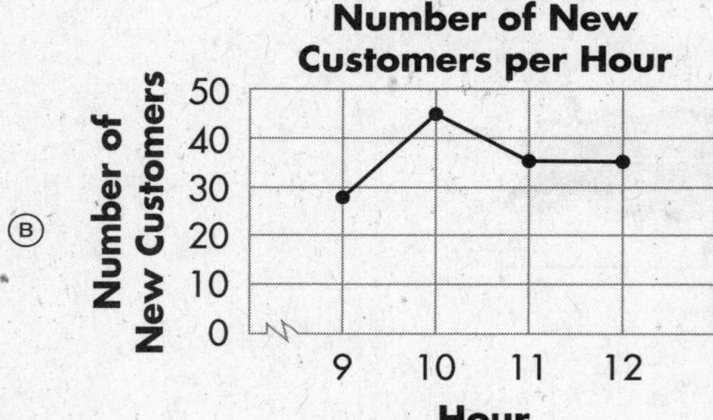

Ⓒ
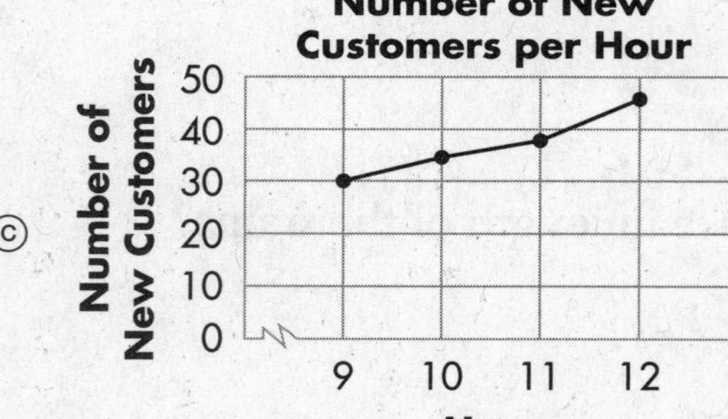

Ⓓ
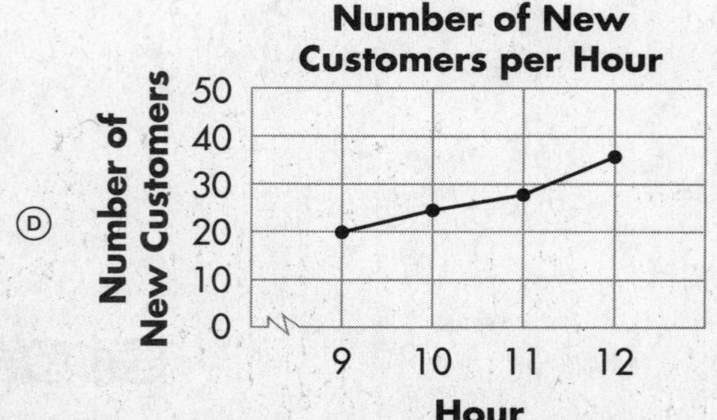

Go On

Name ______________________

35 Describe the pattern of the numbers in the grid below. Explain how you could use the pattern to find the missing numbers.

THINK SOLVE EXPLAIN

0.27				
0.37	0.38	0.39	0.4	
0.47				
0.57				

____

____

____

____

____

____

____

____

____

____

36 Adolpho has a total of 17 shirts. He has 4 brown shirts, b blue shirts, and 6 white shirts. Solve the equation $4 + b + 6 = 17$ to find how many blue shirts Adolpho has.

Ⓕ 5

Ⓖ 7

Ⓗ 10

Ⓘ 17

Go On

37 Marissa has 28 stickers to decorate her journal. The number of stickers she can fit on each page is shown below.

4 stickers per page

Marissa is trying to find how many pages, p, will have stickers on them. Which diagram and equation represents the problem?

Ⓐ $p \div 28 = 4$

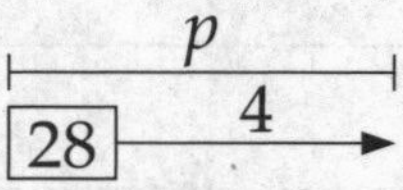

Ⓑ $28 \div 4 = p$

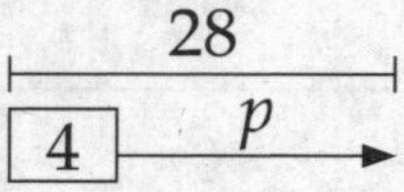

Ⓒ $p \div 4 = 28$

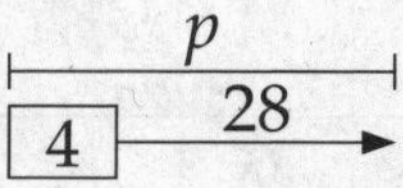

Ⓓ $p \times 28 = 4$

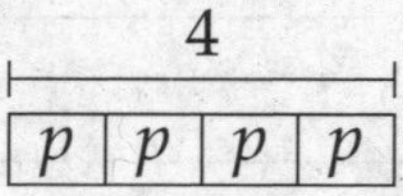

38 Hiro spent \$15 for a painting. He spent \$8 on a frame and \$3 on gift wrapping. At lunch, his sister gave him \$9. At the end of the day, Hiro had \$27. How much did he have at the start of the day?

Ⓕ \$10

Ⓖ \$36

Ⓗ \$41

Ⓘ \$44

Go On

39 What is the distance between $^{-}4$ and $^{+}2$ on the number line below?

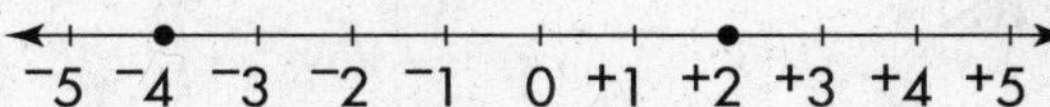

Ⓐ 6 units

Ⓑ 4 units

Ⓒ 3 units

Ⓓ 1 unit

40 Susan started a factor tree to find the prime factorization of 180.

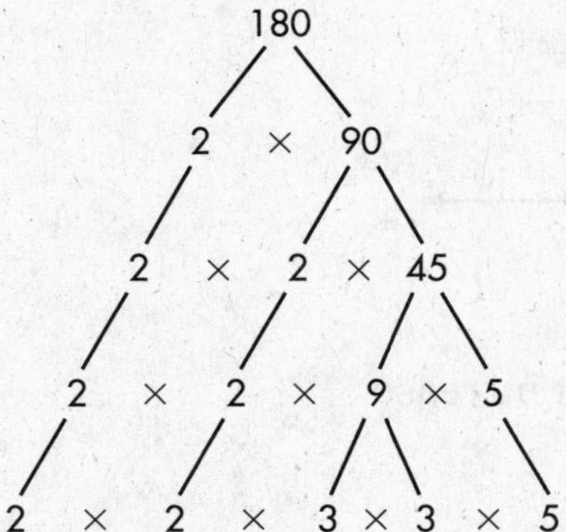

What should Susan write as the prime factorization of 180?

Ⓕ $4 \times 3 \times 5$

Ⓖ $4 \times 3^3 \times 5$

Ⓗ $2^2 \times 3 \times 5^2$

Ⓘ $2^2 \times 3^2 \times 5$

Go On

Name ___________________________________

41 Alisha's doctor keeps a record of her height. At her last appointment, the doctor made a line graph to show Alisha how her height has changed over the years.

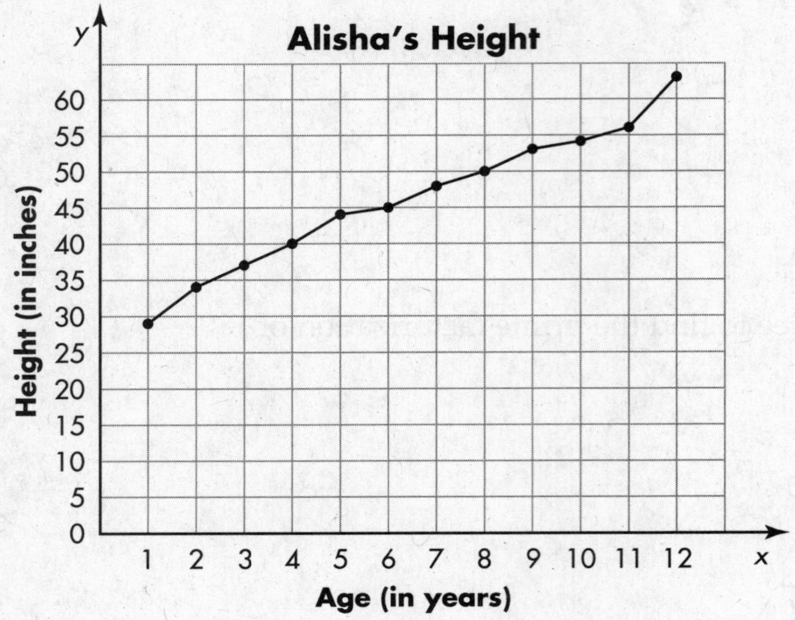

Between which two ages did Alisha's height increase the most?

Ⓐ 1 to 2

Ⓑ 4 to 5

Ⓒ 8 to 9

Ⓓ 11 to 12

Go On

Name ______________________________

42 Clarice bought a hamster for \$3.95, a pet cage for \$7.75, and hamster food for \$2.50. She gave the cashier the money shown below.

How much change should Clarice receive?

Ⓕ \$0.60

Ⓖ \$0.80

Ⓗ \$1.60

Ⓘ \$1.80

43 Mia and Lea picked strawberries to sell at a fruit stand. Lea picked $\frac{3}{4}$ quart. Mia picked $\frac{1}{5}$ quart. How many quarts of strawberries did they pick in all?

Ⓐ $\frac{4}{9}$ quart

Ⓑ $\frac{11}{20}$ quart

Ⓒ $\frac{13}{20}$ quart

Ⓓ $\frac{19}{20}$ quart

Go On

44 The table below shows the record low temperatures of four U.S. cities.

Record Low Temperatures	
City	**Temperature**
Chicago, Illinois	−27°F
Washington, D.C.	−5°F
Jacksonville, Florida	7°F
Memphis, Tennessee	−13°F

Which list shows the cities in order from *highest* temperature to *lowest* temperature?

Ⓕ Jacksonville, Washington, D.C., Memphis, Chicago

Ⓖ Chicago, Jacksonville, Washington, D.C., Memphis

Ⓗ Washington, D.C., Jacksonville, Memphis, Chicago

Ⓘ Chicago, Memphis, Washington, D.C., Jacksonville

45 There are 35 students in the fifth-grade class who will visit the DinoDigs exhibit at the Orlando Science Center. The students can view the exhibit in groups with a maximum of 4 students. What is the least number of groups the fifth-grade class can be put in to?

Ⓐ 10

Ⓑ 9

Ⓒ 8

Ⓓ 7

Go On

46 Ava took a survey to find out which animals the boys and girls in her class liked the best after a class trip to Florida's Lion Country Safari. She made the graph below to show her data.

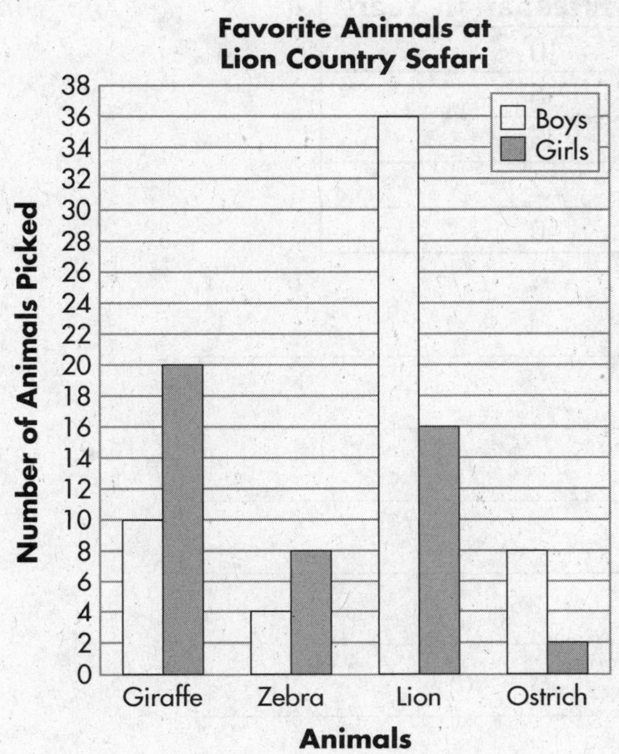

For which animal is there the greatest difference between boys and girls?

Ⓕ Giraffe

Ⓖ Zebra

Ⓗ Lion

Ⓘ Ostrich

Name ______________________________

47 Explain what type of graph would be most appropriate to display the data in the table below.

THINK
SOLVE
EXPLAIN

Average Lifespan of Animals

Animal	Average Lifespan in Years
Rhino	40
American Alligator	56
Lion	35
Tiger	22
Asian Elephant	40

____

____

____

____

____

____

48 The number of innings in a regular baseball game is 9. What is this number in exponential notation?

Ⓐ 3^2

Ⓑ 3^3

Ⓒ 9^2

Ⓓ 3^9

Go On

49 Mindy and her family are going on a picnic. They are taking the cooler shown below.

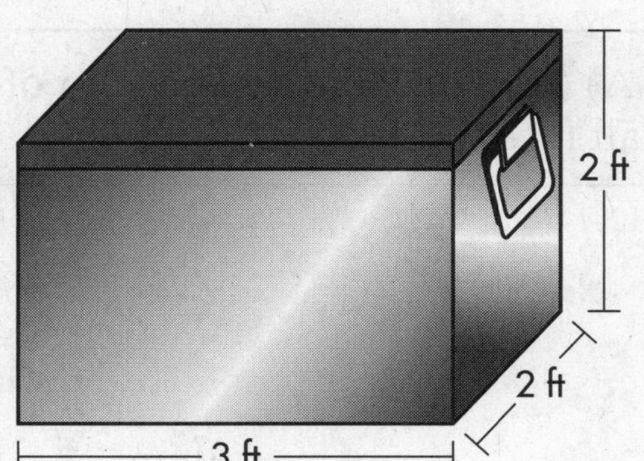

Surface Area (SA) (polyhedron) = The sum of all the areas of all faces

How many square feet is the surface area of the cooler?

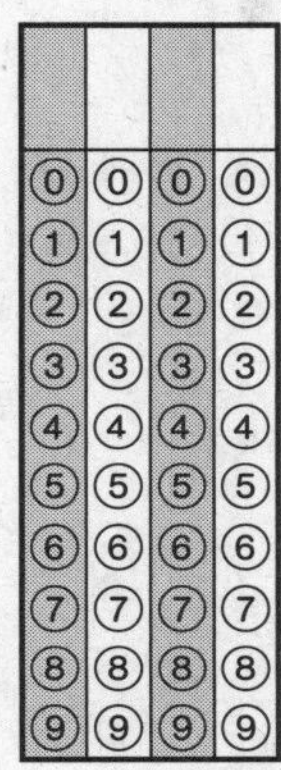

50 The touch tank at Tampa Bay's Florida Aquarium allows visitors to touch sea stars, crabs, urchins, and other sea creatures. The tank has a length of 42 feet, a width of 2 feet, and a height of 4 feet. What is the volume of the tank?

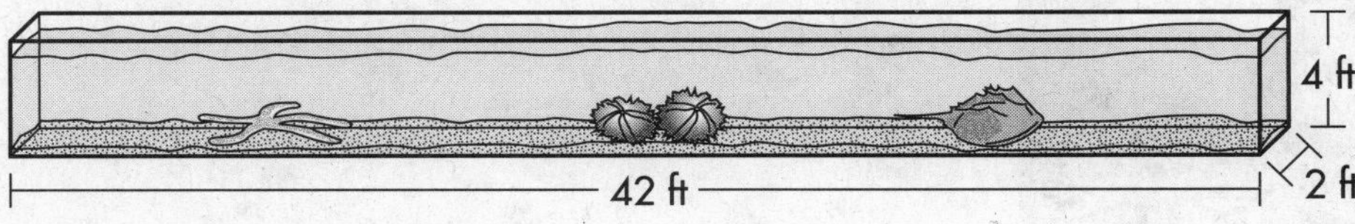

Ⓕ 48 cubic feet

Ⓖ 84 cubic feet

Ⓗ 193 cubic feet

Ⓘ 336 cubic feet

Volume = length × width × height

Go On

51 How can you find the surface area of this figure without adding the areas of all the faces?

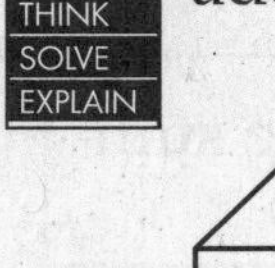

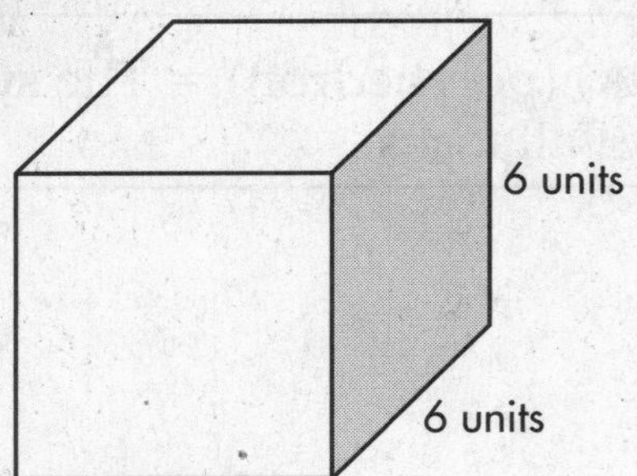

Surface Area (SA) (polyhedron) = The sum of all the areas of all faces

____

____

____

____

____

52 Several artists have completed a mural on an outside wall of a museum. The mural has a base of 10 meters and height of 9 meters. What is the area of the mural?

Area = base × height

Ⓐ 19 square meters

Ⓑ 38 square meters

Ⓒ 90 square meters

Ⓓ 109 square meters

Go On

53 The outdoor concert hall has a section with seats and a grassy section in the shape of a triangle.

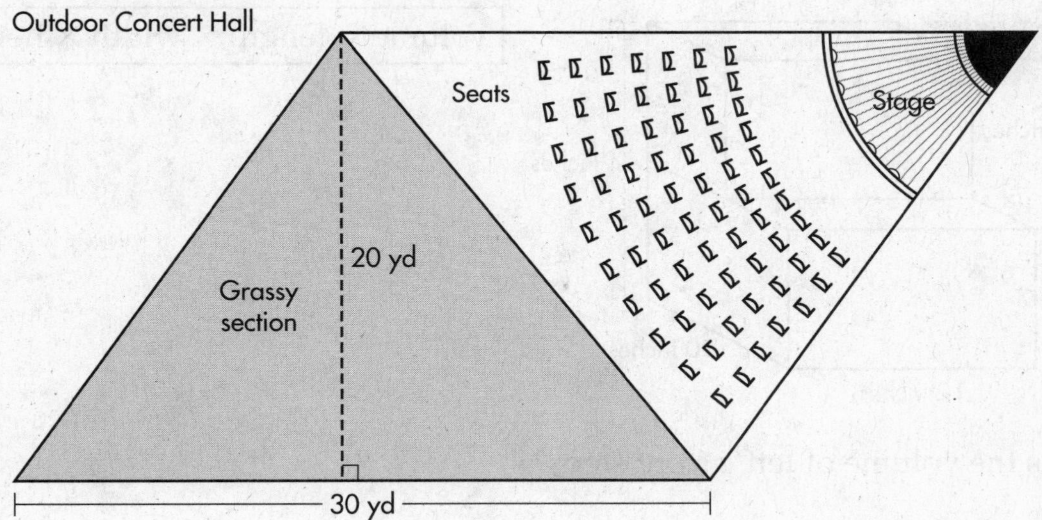

What is the area of the grassy section of the outdoor concert hall?

Ⓕ 50 square yards

Ⓖ 300 square yards

Ⓗ 500 square yards

Ⓘ 600 square yards

$$\text{Area} = \frac{\text{base} \times \text{height}}{2}$$

54 Jeff measured the steps leading to his front door. He wrote the dimensions of the steps below.

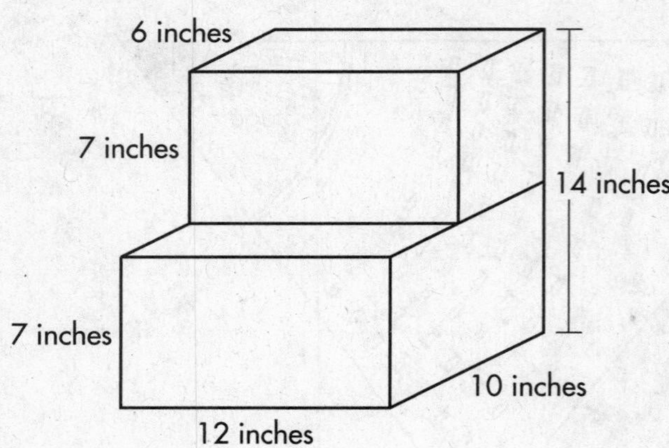

Volume = length × width × height

What is the volume of Jeff's front steps?

Ⓐ 504 cubic inches

Ⓑ 840 cubic inches

Ⓒ 1,200 cubic inches

Ⓓ 1,344 cubic inches

55 Last night, Erin completed $\frac{5}{6}$ of the homework assignment. Tom completed $\frac{1}{3}$ of the same assignment. How much more of the assignment did Erin complete?

Ⓕ $\frac{1}{3}$

Ⓖ $\frac{1}{2}$

Ⓗ $\frac{6}{9}$

Ⓘ $\frac{4}{3}$

Go On

Name ______________________

56 The tongue of a giant anteater can stick 2 feet out of its mouth to capture prey. How long is a giant anteater's tongue in inches?

0	0	0	0
1	1	1	1
2	2	2	2
3	3	3	3
4	4	4	4
5	5	5	5
6	6	6	6
7	7	7	7
8	8	8	8
9	9	9	9

1 foot = 12 inches

57 What is the ordered pair for Point *W*?

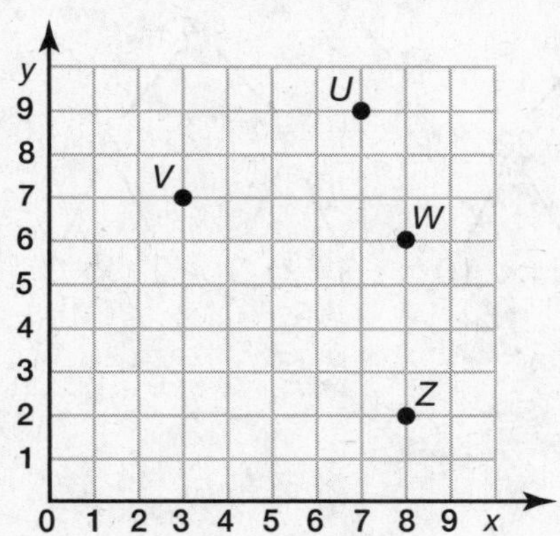

Ⓐ (8, 6)

Ⓑ (6, 8)

Ⓒ (8, 2)

Ⓓ (7, 9)

Go On

58 Justin is 4 years older than his sister Carla. The equation $y = x + 4$ represents the relationship between Justin and Carla's age. Which ordered pair will be included on the graph for $y = x + 4$?

Ⓕ (0, 0)

Ⓖ (9, 13)

Ⓗ (12, 3)

Ⓘ (12, 8)

59 Which of the factor trees does NOT show a prime factorization?

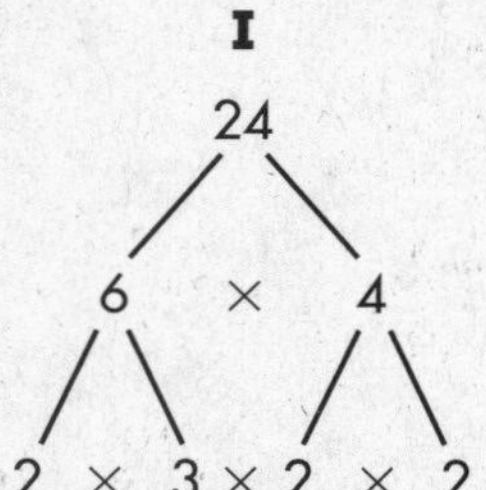

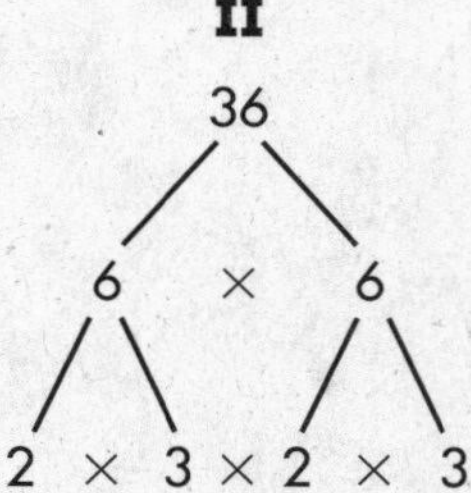

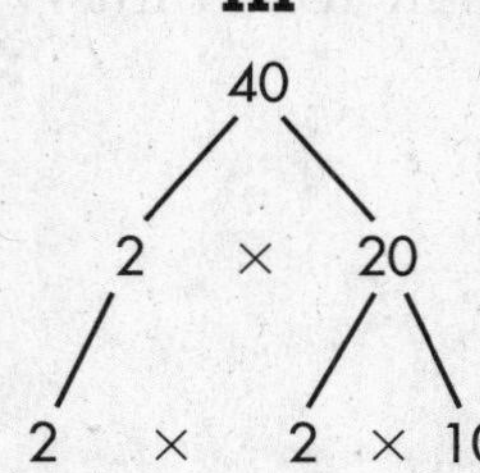

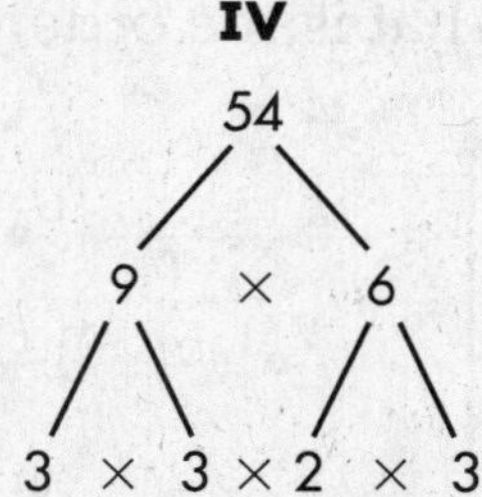

Ⓐ I

Ⓑ II

Ⓒ III

Ⓓ IV

Go On

Name ______________________

60 Emily jogged $\frac{7}{10}$ mile and sprinted $\frac{1}{10}$ mile. In simplest form, how much farther did she jog than sprint?

Ⓕ $\frac{6}{10}$ mile

Ⓖ $\frac{4}{5}$ mile

Ⓗ $\frac{7}{10}$ mile

Ⓘ $\frac{3}{5}$ mile

61 Mr. Larkin drew the solid below along with a view of the solid for his students.

Solid

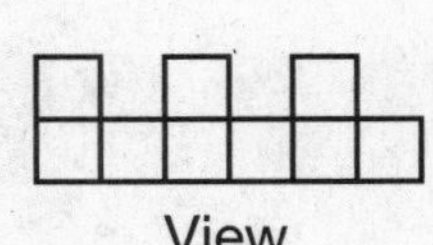
View

Which view of the solid did Mr. Larkin draw for his students?

Ⓐ Front view

Ⓑ Back view

Ⓒ Side view

Ⓓ Top view

Go On

62 It takes 4 yards of material to make one curtain. How many curtains can Diane make out of 30 yards and how much material will be left over?

Ⓕ She can make 7 curtains with 2 yards left over.

Ⓖ She can make 7 curtains with 0 yards left over.

Ⓗ She can make 6 curtains with 2 yards left over.

Ⓘ She can make 6 curtains with 7 yards left over.

63 Which number line shows Point F at $^{-}7$?

Ⓐ F
$^{-}10$ $^{-}8$ $^{-}6$ $^{-}4$ $^{-}2$ 0 $^{+}2$ $^{+}4$ $^{+}6$ $^{+}8$ $^{+}10$

Ⓑ F
$^{-}10$ $^{-}8$ $^{-}6$ $^{-}4$ $^{-}2$ 0 $^{+}2$ $^{+}4$ $^{+}6$ $^{+}8$ $^{+}10$

Ⓒ F
$^{-}10$ $^{-}8$ $^{-}6$ $^{-}4$ $^{-}2$ 0 $^{+}2$ $^{+}4$ $^{+}6$ $^{+}8$ $^{+}10$

Ⓓ F
$^{-}10$ $^{-}8$ $^{-}6$ $^{-}4$ $^{-}2$ 0 $^{+}2$ $^{+}4$ $^{+}6$ $^{+}8$ $^{+}10$

Go On

64 Yao used $\frac{5}{3}$ sheets of paper on his math assignment. What is this number written as a mixed number?

Ⓕ $1\frac{1}{3}$

Ⓖ $1\frac{2}{3}$

Ⓗ $2\frac{3}{5}$

Ⓘ $2\frac{2}{3}$

65 The map shows only the Northeast and Southeast regions of the United States.

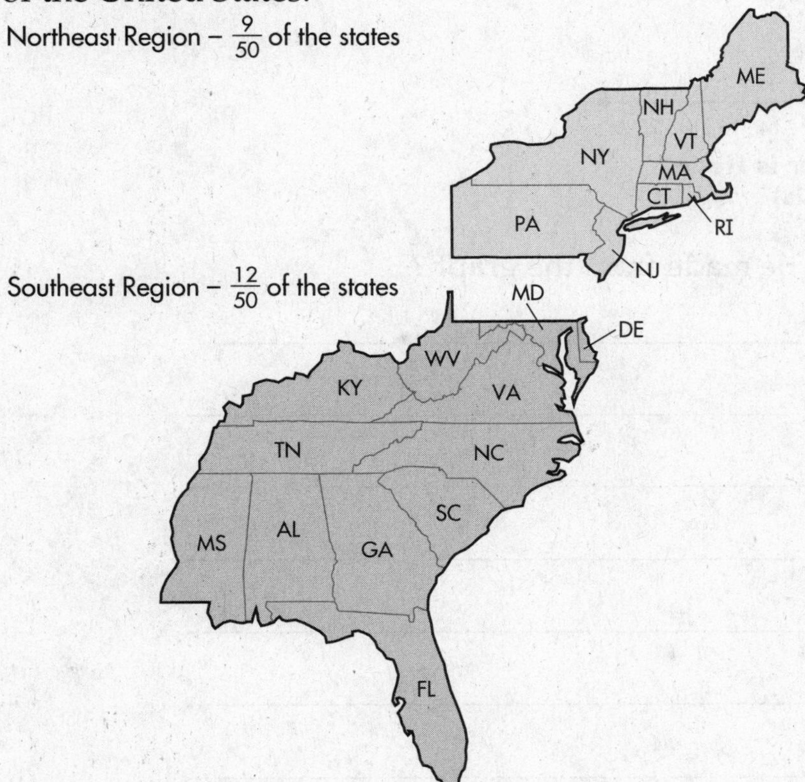

What fraction of the states is in the Northeast and Southeast regions?

Ⓐ $\frac{12}{100}$

Ⓑ $\frac{21}{100}$

Ⓒ $\frac{9}{50}$

Ⓓ $\frac{21}{50}$

Go On

Name ______________________

66 THINK SOLVE EXPLAIN During a thunderstorm, lightning can be seen before thunder is heard. By counting the seconds between seeing the lightning and hearing the thunder, one can determine how far away the lightning strike was. The graph below shows the relationship between a person's distance from lightning and the number of seconds that pass until thunder is heard.

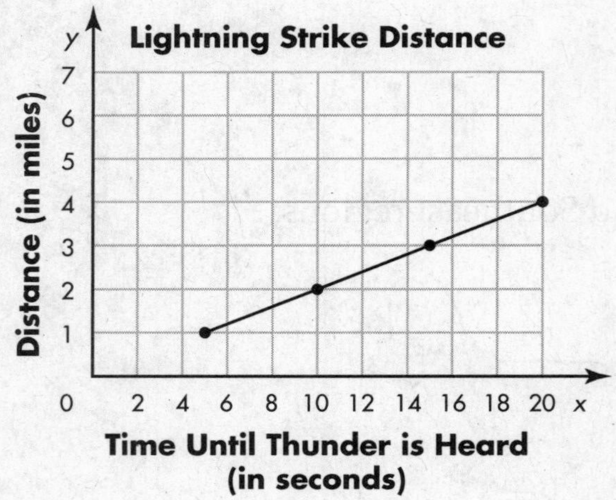

What conclusions can be made from the graph?

____

____

____

____

____

____

____

____

____

Go On

Name ______________________

67 Cosmonaut Valery Bykovsky flew aboard Vostok 5 for 120 hours. Which of the following is shorter than 120 hours?

- Ⓕ 1 day
- Ⓖ 1 week
- Ⓗ 1 month
- Ⓘ 1 year

68 The Johnsons sold 15 bushels of corn in 1 hour at a local farmer's market.

If 1 bushel weighs 56 pounds, how many ounces does 1 bushel weigh?

1 pound = 16 ounces

- Ⓐ 896 ounces
- Ⓑ 720 ounces
- Ⓒ 420 ounces
- Ⓓ 128 ounces

Go On

Name ___________________________________

69 Kyle's frog made two jumps. Kyle measured the length of his frog's two jumps, in meters, and showed the distances on the number line below.

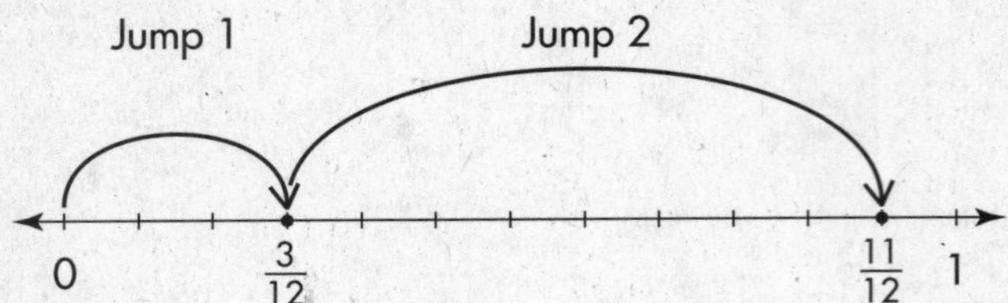

How far did Kyle's frog jump during Jump 2?

Ⓕ 1 meter

Ⓖ $\frac{12}{13}$ meter

Ⓗ $\frac{2}{3}$ meter

Ⓘ $\frac{1}{4}$ meter

70 The top of the Washington Monument in Washington, D.C., forms a pyramid. The triangular faces all have the same area. The base and height of the faces, to the nearest foot, are shown below.

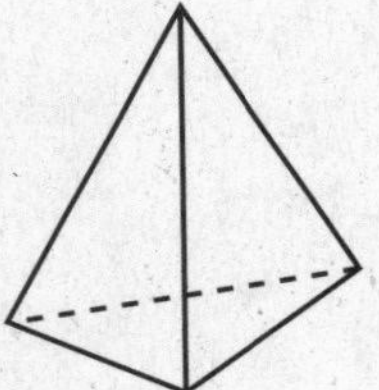

$$\text{Area} = \frac{\text{base} \times \text{height}}{2}$$

What is the area of each triangular face of the pyramid?

Ⓐ 1,870 square feet

Ⓑ 935 square feet

Ⓒ 623 square feet

Ⓓ 92 square feet

STOP

End-of-Year Test Topics **1–16**

Name ______________________________

1 How many faces, edges, and vertices are in the pyramid below?

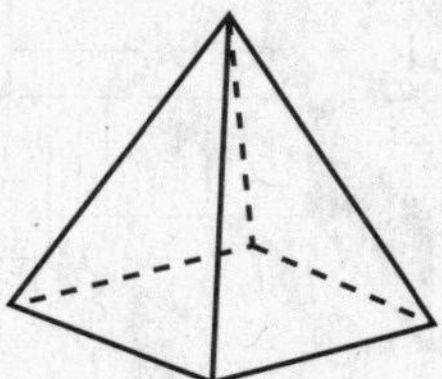

Ⓐ 5 faces, 8 edges, 5 vertices

Ⓑ 5 faces, 12 edges, 5 vertices

Ⓒ 6 faces, 8 edges, 6 vertices

Ⓓ 6 faces, 12 edges, 6 vertices

2 Which of the following is a triangular prism?

Ⓕ 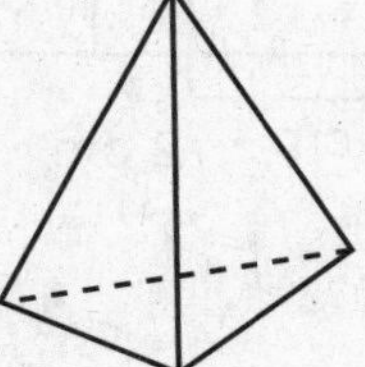

Ⓗ 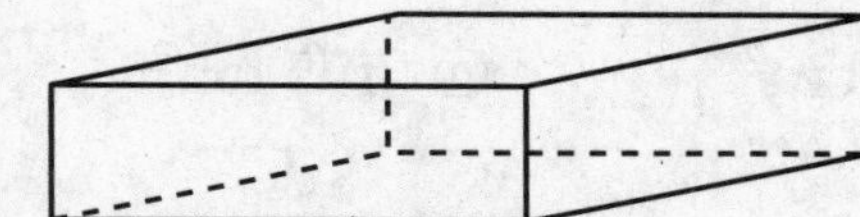

Ⓖ 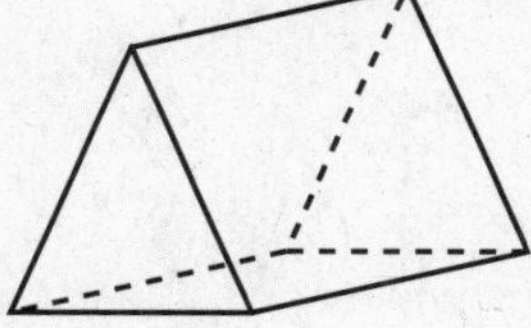

Ⓘ 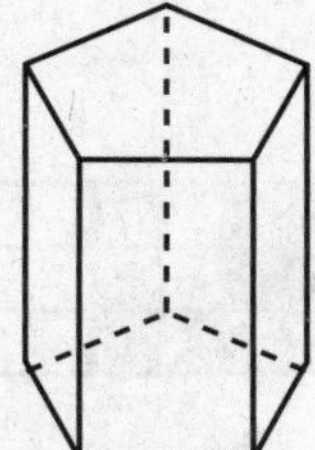

3 What solid can be made using the net below?

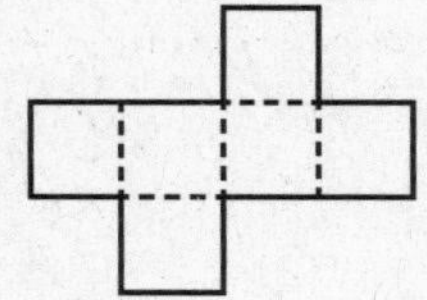

Ⓐ Cylinder

Ⓑ Rectangular pyramid

Ⓒ Cone

Ⓓ Cube

Go On

Name ______________________

4 A store manager stacked some cubes for a display as shown at the right. Which of the following is the front view of the cubes?

Ⓕ 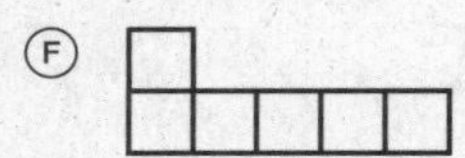

Ⓗ 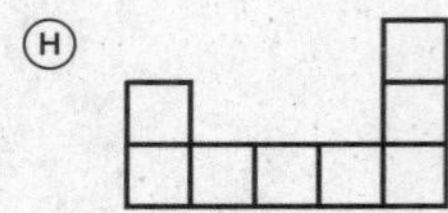

Ⓖ 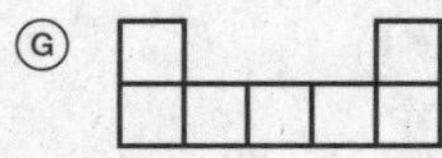

Ⓘ 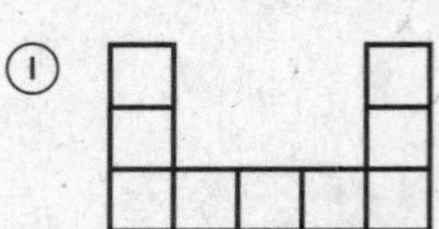

5 Jared unfolded a gift box as shown below. What is the surface area of the box?

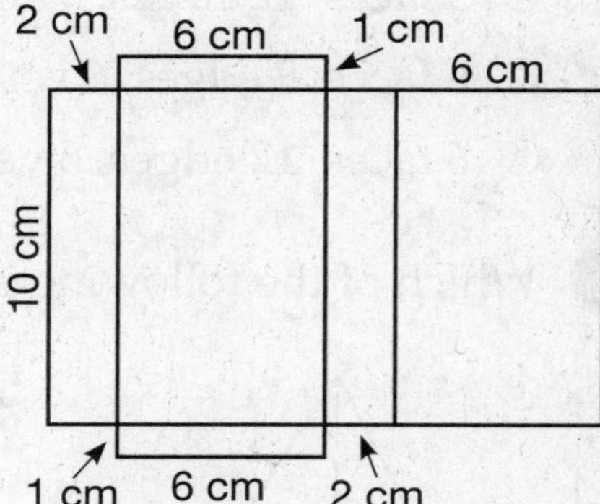

Surface area = the sum of the areas of all the faces.

Ⓐ 55 cm^2

Ⓑ 120 cm^2

Ⓒ 172 cm^2

Ⓓ 175 cm^2

6 What are the volume and surface area of the solid shown below? You can use the net to help find the surface area. Explain how you found your answers.

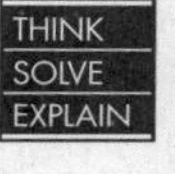

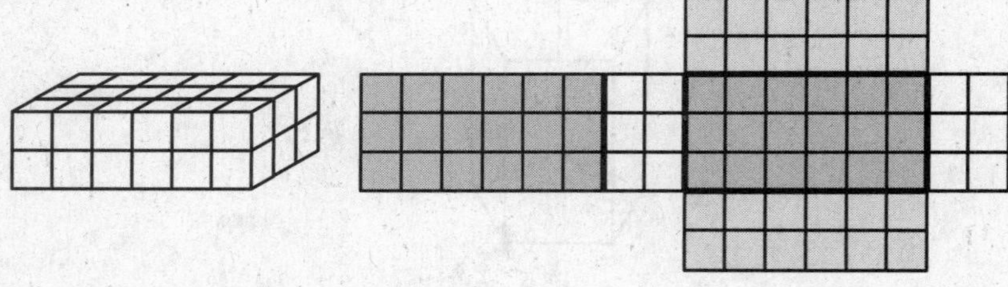

____

____

____

____

____

____

____

Go On

7 The Kims ordered furniture for their porch. The furniture came in a box similar to the one below.

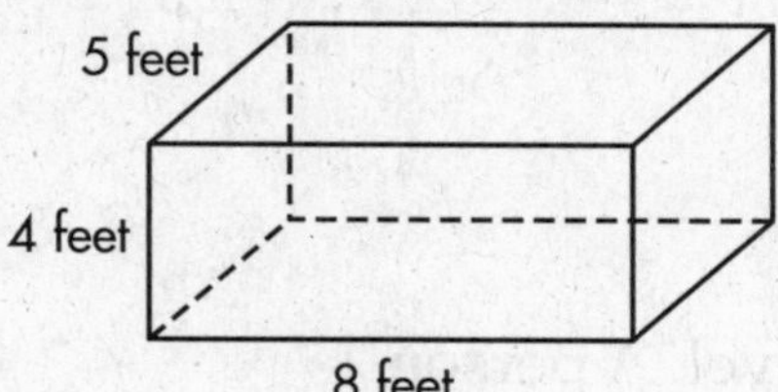

Volume = length × width × height

How many cubic feet is the volume of the box?

8 Rubio makes steps for his sister's dollhouse. What is the volume of the steps shown below?

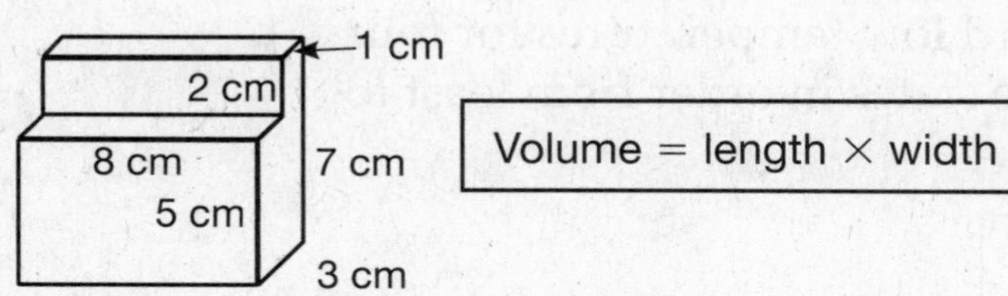

Volume = length × width × height

Ⓕ 920 cm^3

Ⓖ 640 cm^3

Ⓗ 168 cm^3

Ⓘ 136 cm^3

9 What is the surface area of the solid shown at the right? Each cube measures 1 cm × 1 cm × 1 cm.

Surface area = the sum of the areas of all the faces.

Ⓐ 64 cm^2

Ⓑ 22 cm^2

Ⓒ 16 cm^2

Ⓓ 11 cm^2

10 The highest temperature ever recorded in Florida was 109°F. What is the opposite of $^{+}109$?

Ⓕ $^{+}110$ Ⓗ $^{-}109$

Ⓖ $^{+}109$ Ⓘ $^{-}108$

11 Near the shore, a swimmer is 4 feet below sea level. A person watching from a paddle boat is 5 feet above sea level. What is the distance between the swimmer and the person watching from the boat?

Ⓐ 1 foot Ⓒ 5 feet

Ⓑ 4 feet Ⓓ 9 feet

12 Which point on the number line can represent the temperature 6 degrees below 0?

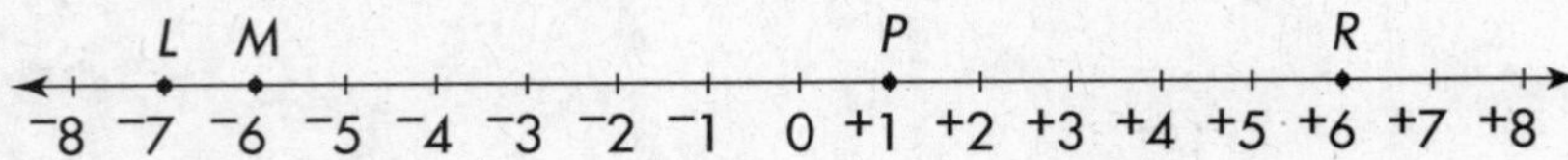

Ⓕ Point *L* Ⓗ Point *P*

Ⓖ Point *M* Ⓘ Point *R*

13 The table below shows the record low temperatures for four U.S. states. Which list shows the states in order from least to greatest temperature?

U.S. Record Low Temperatures	
State	**Temperature**
Florida	$^{-}2$°F
Hawaii	12°F
North Carolina	$^{-}34$°F
Maryland	$^{-}40$°F

Ⓐ Hawaii, Florida, North Carolina, Maryland

Ⓑ Florida, North Carolina, Maryland, Hawaii

Ⓒ Maryland, North Carolina, Florida, Hawaii

Ⓓ Hawaii, Maryland, North Carolina, Florida

Go On

Name ______________________________

14 Roberto made the figures below from square tiles. How many square tiles will Roberto need for his seventh figure?

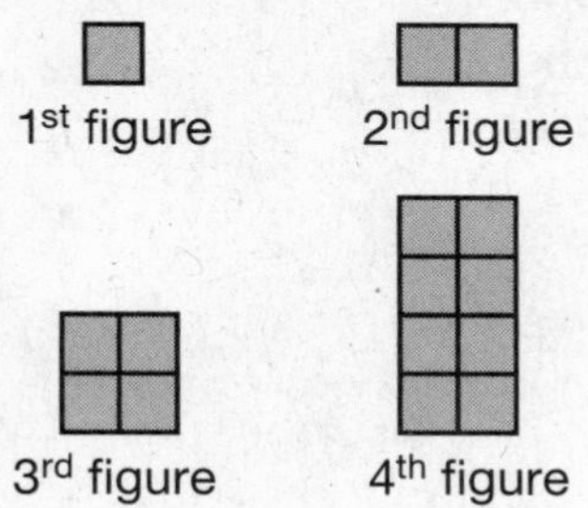

Ⓕ 64 Ⓗ 16

Ⓖ 32 Ⓘ 12

15 Jaime is playing a game that uses numbered spaces 1–100. During one of his turns, he moves forward 4 spaces, back 6 spaces, and forward 11 spaces. He ends up on Space 27. What numbered space did he begin on?

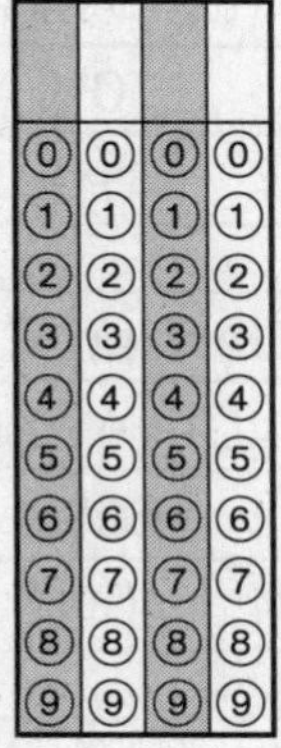

16 The double-bar graph compares the populations of the continents of North America and South America. In what year was the greatest population difference between North America and South America?

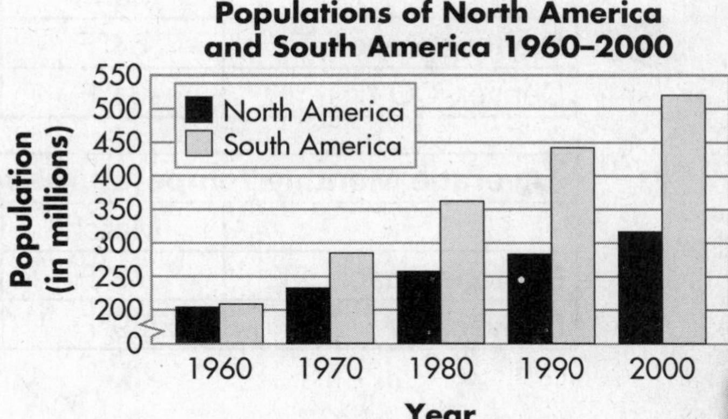

Ⓐ 1960 Ⓒ 1990

Ⓑ 1980 Ⓓ 2000

Go On

Name ______________________________

17 The double-bar graph below shows average monthly temperatures for Daytona Beach, FL, and Denver, CO. Which table correctly shows the data for the graph?

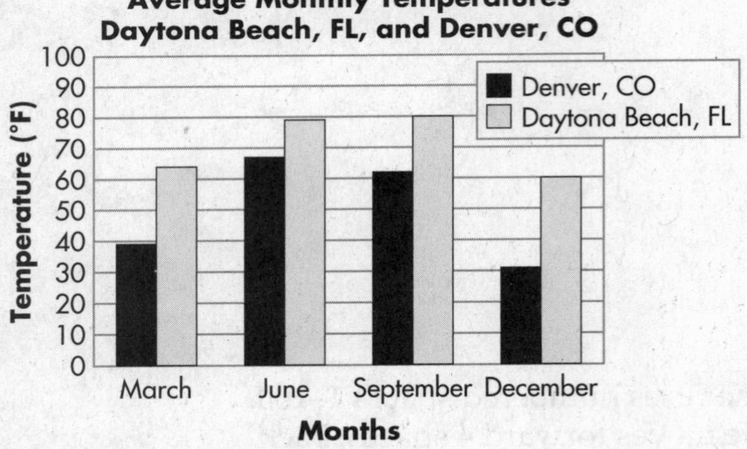

Ⓕ

Average Monthly Temperatures for Daytona Beach, FL, and Denver, CO				
	March	June	September	December
Daytona Beach, FL	74°F	89°F	90°F	70°F
Denver, CO	49°F	77°F	72°F	41°F

Ⓖ

Average Monthly Temperatures for Daytona Beach, FL, and Denver, CO				
	March	June	September	December
Daytona Beach, FL	64°F	79°F	80°F	60°F
Denver, CO	39°F	67°F	62°F	31°F

Ⓗ

Average Monthly Temperatures for Daytona Beach, FL, and Denver, CO				
	March	June	September	December
Daytona Beach, FL	64°F	79°F	80°F	60°F
Denver, CO	31°F	62°F	67°F	39°F

Ⓘ

Average Monthly Temperatures for Daytona Beach, FL, and Denver, CO				
	March	June	September	December
Daytona Beach, FL	79°F	60°F	64°F	80°F
Denver, CO	39°F	67°F	62°F	31°F

Go On

Name ______________________________

18 Catie babysits on the weekends. She made a line graph to show the total amount of money she earned after five days. Between which two days did Catie see the greatest increase in her total earnings?

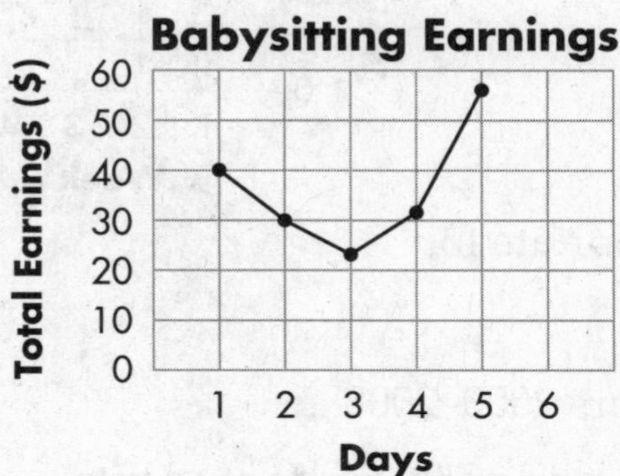

Ⓐ Day 1 and Day 2
Ⓑ Day 2 and Day 3
Ⓒ Day 3 and Day 4
Ⓓ Day 4 and Day 5

19 The bar graph shows some of the most common city names in the United States. All of these city names are also found in Florida. How many cities by the name of Springfield are there in the United States?

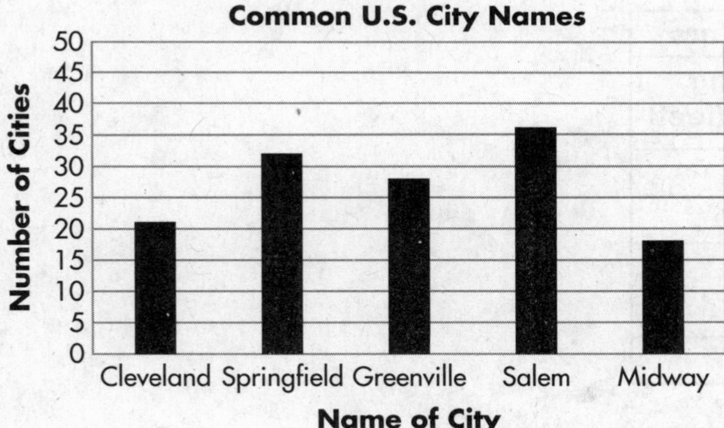

Ⓕ 32
Ⓖ 28
Ⓗ 21
Ⓘ 18

Go On

Name ___________________________________

20 Rico recorded the weight of his puppy over 4 weeks. How many pounds did his puppy weigh at 3 weeks?

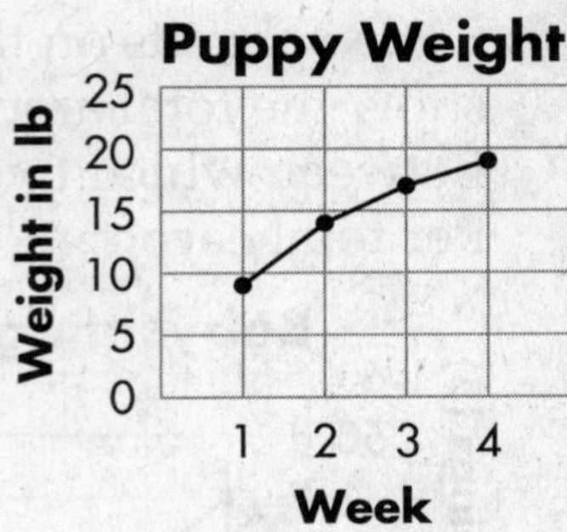

Ⓐ 19 pounds

Ⓑ 17 pounds

Ⓒ 14 pounds

Ⓓ 9 pounds

21 A double-bar graph would be the most appropriate for which description?

Ⓕ The attendance at a theme park for the years 2000–2008

Ⓖ Results of a survey of favorite pets of fifth- and sixth-grade students

Ⓗ Heights of six mountain ranges around the world

Ⓘ Results of a survey of favorite snack foods of fifth-grade students

22 THINK SOLVE EXPLAIN

The data in the table shows the speed of a car and the distance it takes to stop once the brakes are applied. What trend or trends can be found? Make a line graph to the right of the table, and use it to explain your answer.

Stopping Distances for Cars	
Speed (miles/hour)	Stopping Distance (feet)
10	15
20	40
30	75
40	120
50	175

____

____

____

____

____

STOP